Revis

Questions

for

National 5

Physics

Campbell White

Formerly Principal Teacher of Physics
Tynecastle High School, Edinburgh

Published by
Chemcord
Inch Keith
East Kilbride
Glasgow

ISBN 9781870570992

Acknowledgement
We would like to thank Jim Page, formerly Principal
Teacher of Physics at Queen Anne High School,
Dunfermline for his help in the editing of the early stages
of this book.

Printed by Bell and Bain Ltd, Glasgow

Contents

Introduction to National 5 Physics

About the book

The questions in this book cover all the key areas of National 5 Physics for the three Units of the Course. In addition, some questions relate to content of National 4 Physics. These are judged to be useful as an introduction to the content of National 5.

Some questions that go beyond the key areas of National 5 Physics have also been included. These questions are designed to test your background Physics knowledge, so that you are better able to answer the open-ended questions that are included in the Course assessment. Open-ended questions can be recognised because they will usually say something like "Using your knowledge of Physics, comment on ...".

The answers to numerical questions are given at the end of the book.
A separate answer book, which contains full answers to all the questions, is available. The question and answer books together form an aid that enables you to *actively* assess your knowledge and understanding of the National 5 Physics Course.

Physical quantities and SI units

Measurement is at the heart of all work in Physics. The SI (Systeme International) system of units is almost universally used today. In the SI system, certain basic units of measurement of physical quantities are defined and from these defined units, others are derived. The main defined units that are needed for National 5 Physics are as follows:

- **length** – metre (m)
- **time** – second (s)
- **mass** – kilogram (kg)

All the physical quantities that you will meet in National 5 Physics are listed in the table on pages vi and vii. Copy and complete each row in the table as you come across the quantity in your work.

The unit of electric current is also a defined unit, and the unit of temperature defined in the SI system is the kelvin (K), although the degree Celsius (°C) is in more common use for most branches of Physics. Both of these units of temperature are used as appropriate throughout this book.

In this book, derived units are written with a negative power, e.g. $m\ s^{-1}$ is used for the unit of velocity, 'metre per second'. The unit of velocity can also correctly be written as m/s.

All the relationships that you will meet in National 5 Physics are listed on pages viii / ix.

Scientific notation

Many quantities in Physics are either very small or very large. For example, the speed of light in air is three hundred million metres per second, while the wavelength of light is about 0.000 000 7 m.

Numbers such as this can be written in one of the ways given above – as words or with a string of zeros before or after a decimal point. There is a disadvantage with each of these methods: numbers in words are not easy to visualise or to manipulate, and it is very easy to make a mistake in the positioning of the decimal point when a very large or a very small number is written out with zeros.

Both of these disadvantages are eliminated by the use of **scientific notation**. With scientific notation a number is usually written as a number between 1 and 10 multiplied by a suitable power of ten.

three hundred million $= 3 \times 10^8$
$0.000\ 000\ 7 = 7 \times 10^{-7}$

On a calculator the $\boxed{\text{EXP}}$ button means 'times ten to the power of —'.

Numbers expressed in scientific notation are usually keyed into a calculator as:

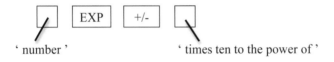

' number '   ' times ten to the power of '

e.g. 5×10^{-3} is keyed in as:

$\boxed{5}$ $\boxed{\text{EXP}}$ $\boxed{+/-}$ $\boxed{3}$

It is equally important to interpret correctly an answer given in scientific notation on a calculator. An answer of 5×10^{-3} may be shown exactly that way on the display of the calculator. More often it will be displayed as 5 -3, 05 -03, 5^{-3}, 5^{-03}, or 5 E-3. Remember that all of these forms mean 5×10^{-3} and should be given this way in the final answer to any question.

Prefixes

The SI system of units is based on powers of ten and uses a system of prefixes that indicate the multiple or sub-unit being used.

You should know the following prefixes.

nano (n)	10^{-9}	giga (G)	10^{9}
micro (μ)	10^{-6}	mega (M)	10^{6}
milli (m)	10^{-3}	kilo (k)	10^{3}

Examples of the use of these prefixes are given below.
There are 1000 millimetres (1 mm = 10^{-3} m) in 1 metre.
A voltage of 1 volt across a resistor of value 1 megohm (1 MΩ = 10^{6} Ω) causes a current of 1 microamp (1 μA = 10^{-6} A).
The power of a domestic electric fire is about 1 kilowatt (1000 W = 1 kW) while that associated with a power station is about 1 gigawatt (1 000 000 000 W = 1 GW).

Significant figures

When a calculator is used to divide 56.4 (**three** significant figures) by 23 (**two** significant figures), the display will give one of the following answers, depending on the number of digits in the calculator display.

2.4521739
2.45217391
2.452173913

Since each of the original numbers was given to fewer significant figures than on the calculator display, to quote the calculator answer is incorrect because it suggests that the answer is known to eight, nine or even ten significant figures. In carrying out calculations, it is important to give answers to an appropriate number of significant figures. This means that the final answer should have no more significant figures than the value with least number of significant figures used in a calculation, i.e. you should give this answer as 2.5 (two significant figures).

Answering numerical questions

It is easy to cut corners with numerical questions by leaving out working – but it is also easy to lose marks if you do this. Standard numerical questions in the National 5 Course assessment are worth 3 marks: 1 mark for stating the correct relationship, 1 mark for correct substitution and 1 mark for the correct answer. If you do not show your working and your answer is wrong, you will be given no marks. However, if your method is correct and you have only made an arithmetical mistake then, if you have shown all of your working, you might only lose a mark.

Follow the stages set out in the following example for all numerical problems.

> During a qualifying run for a Grand Prix, a driver took 1 minute 26.275 seconds to complete one lap of the circuit. The length of the circuit is 4.309 km.
>
> Calculate his average speed for this lap.

For numerical questions, read the question and write down the given information as quantity, symbol, value and unit. If the unit given is not the basic SI unit, then convert to SI.

> time t = 1 minute 26.275 s = 86.275 s
> distance d = 4.309 km = 4309 m
> speed v = ?

Decide which relationship to use by considering the information given and the quantity to be found. Writing down the relationship will gain you the first mark.

$$\text{average speed} = \frac{\text{total distance}}{\text{total time}} \qquad \bar{v} = \frac{d}{t}$$

Substitute the given numbers for the quantities in the relationship and rearrange if necessary. This will gain you the second mark.

$$\bar{v} = \frac{4309}{86.275}$$

Complete the calculation and write down the answer with the correct units and giving the correct number of significant figures for the final mark.

$$\bar{v} = \frac{4309}{86.275} = 49.94 \text{ m s}^{-1}$$

In this example, four significant figures should be given because the value for distance is given to four significant figures. The value for the speed is given to five significant figures.

Introduction to Physics

Answering other types of questions

With non-numerical questions, for example, a description of an experiment, answer the question that is asked not the one that you hoped would be asked. So if the question asks for a description of an experiment to calculate the instantaneous speed of a trolley, do not write about two light gates separated by several metres – this would give an average speed.

It might be obvious but it is worth noting – if you leave a multiple choice question blank you will gain no marks. With a guess you have a one in five chance of being correct. But the best solution of all is to know the work well enough to be able to answer without guessing.

Read what you are being told to do in a question. 'Calculate' tells you to use a relationship to work out an answer. 'State' simply asks you to write down what you understand about a part of Physics whereas for an 'explain' question you should answer why some part of Physics is as it is.

If you need to use a value that is not given in a question (the speed of sound in air for example) then use the value given on the Data Sheet of the assessment. A mark will probably be given for using this value in the question. You do not need to memorise any values for physical constants, you should look up any such values in the Data Sheet. A Data Sheet is included on pages x / xi.

As you progress in Physics you will find that you begin to have a feel for the relationships you are working with and you will often be able to tell if an answer 'looks' correct. This is the stage at which you begin to gain an understanding of Physics. This understanding is helped if you can build up an idea or a picture in your mind of the quantities used in Physics and it will go some way in allowing you to check that your answers to calculations are at least possible – say of the correct order of magnitude. Train yourself to look at all your answers to check whether or not the answer seems reasonable.

This 'feel' for Physics comes from various sources.
For example, the following may be useful to help to build up an understanding.
- A bag of sugar has a mass of 1 kilogram.
- A newton is the approximate weight of an apple.
- The currents associated with electronic circuits are in the milli- or microamp ranges.
- A fast runner takes about 10 seconds to run a 100 metre race.

Physical Quantities

The quantities that you will meet in National 5 Physics are listed in the table below. Copy and complete each row in the table as you come across the quantity in your work.

PHYSICAL QUANTITY	SYMBOL	UNIT and ABBREVIATION
Basic SI Units mass	*m*	kilogram kg
length (distance; displacement; height)	*d, s, h*	metre m
time	*t*	second s
Other SI Units absorbed dose		
acceleration		
acceleration due to gravity		
activity of a radioactive source		
area		
average speed, average velocity		
electrical charge		
electrical current		
electrical energy		
energy		
equivalent dose		
equivalent dose rate		
force		
frequency		
gravitational field strength		
gravitational potential energy		
half life		
heat energy		
kinetic energy		
number of nuclei decaying		

PHYSICAL QUANTITY	SYMBOL	UNIT and ABBREVIATION
period		
potential energy		
power		
pressure		
radiation weighting factor		
resistance		
specific heat capacity		
specific latent heat		
speed, velocity		
temperature (degrees centigrade)		
temperature (kelvins)		
voltage, potential difference		
volume		
wavelength		
weight		
work done		

Relationships

Energy

work done = force × distance $E_w = Fd$

power = $\dfrac{\text{energy}}{\text{time}}$ $P = \dfrac{E}{t}$

gravitational potential energy = mgh $E_p = mgh$

kinetic energy = $\frac{1}{2}mv^2$ $E_k = \frac{1}{2}mv^2$

heat = $cm\Delta T$ (for a change in temperature) $E_h = cm\Delta T$

heat = ml (for a change in state) $E_h = ml$

Electricity

charge = current × time $Q = It$

voltage = current × resistance $V = IR$

power = current × voltage $P = IV = I^2R = \dfrac{V^2}{R}$

electrical energy = current × time × voltage $E_e = ItV$

resistors in series $R_T = R_1 + R_2 + R_3 + ...$

resistors in parallel $\dfrac{1}{R_T} = \dfrac{1}{R_1} + \dfrac{1}{R_2} + \dfrac{1}{R_3} + ...$

voltage divider $\dfrac{V_1}{V_2} = \dfrac{R_1}{R_2}$

$V_2 = \left(\dfrac{R_2}{R_1 + R_2} \right) V_s$

Gas laws

pressure = $\dfrac{\text{force}}{\text{area}}$ $p = \dfrac{F}{A}$

pressure – volume law (Boyle's Law) $p_1V_1 = p_2V_2$

pressure – temperature law (the Pressure Law) $\dfrac{p_1}{T_1} = \dfrac{p_2}{T_2}$

volume – temperature law (Charles' Law) $\dfrac{V_1}{T_1} = \dfrac{V_2}{T_2}$

general gas law $\dfrac{p_1V_1}{T_1} = \dfrac{p_2V_2}{T_2}$

Introduction to Physics

Waves

wave speed $= \dfrac{\text{distance}}{\text{time}}$ $\qquad\qquad v = \dfrac{d}{t}$

wave frequency $= \dfrac{\text{number of waves}}{\text{time}}$ $\qquad f = \dfrac{N}{t}$

wave speed = frequency × wavelength $\qquad v = f\lambda$

wave period $= \dfrac{1}{\text{frequency}}$ $\qquad\qquad T = \dfrac{1}{f}$

Radiation

activity $= \dfrac{\text{number of disintegrations}}{\text{time}}$ $\qquad A = \dfrac{N}{t}$

absorbed dose $= \dfrac{\text{energy}}{\text{mass}}$ $\qquad\qquad D = \dfrac{E}{m}$

equivalent dose = absorbed dose × radiation weighting factor $\qquad H = Dw_r$

equivalent dose rate $= \dfrac{\text{equivalent dose}}{\text{time}}$ $\qquad \dot{H} = \dfrac{H}{t}$

Dynamics

speed $= \dfrac{\text{distance}}{\text{time}}$ $\qquad\qquad v = \dfrac{d}{t}$

average speed $= \dfrac{\text{total distance}}{\text{total time}}$ $\qquad \bar{v} = \dfrac{d}{t}$

velocity $= \dfrac{\text{displacement}}{\text{time}}$ $\qquad\qquad v = \dfrac{s}{t}$

average velocity $= \dfrac{\text{total displacement}}{\text{total time}}$ $\qquad \bar{v} = \dfrac{s}{t}$

acceleration $= \dfrac{\text{change in velocity}}{\text{time}}$ $\qquad a = \dfrac{\Delta v}{t} = \dfrac{v - u}{t}$

weight = mass × acceleration due to gravity $\qquad W = mg$

unbalanced force = mass × acceleration $\qquad F = ma$

projectile motion (constant horizontal velocity) $\qquad v_h = \dfrac{s}{t}$

projectile motion (constant vertical acceleration) $\qquad v_v = u + at$

Data Sheet

Speed of light in materials

Material	Speed in m s^{-1}
Air	3.0×10^8
Carbon dioxide	3.0×10^8
Diamond	1.2×10^8
Glass	2.0×10^8
Glycerol	2.1×10^8
Water	2.3×10^8

Speed of sound in materials

Material	Speed in m s^{-1}
Aluminium	5200
Air	340
Bone	4100
Carbon dioxide	270
Glycerol	1900
Muscle	1600
Steel	5200
Tissue	1500
Water	1500

Gravitational field strengths

Body	Gravitational field strength on the surface in N kg^{-1}
Earth	9.8
Jupiter	23
Mars	3.7
Mercury	3.7
Moon	1.6
Neptune	11
Saturn	9.0
Sun	270
Uranus	8.7
Venus	8.9

Radiation weighting factors

Type of radiation	Radiation weighting factor
alpha	20
beta	1
fast neutrons	10
gamma	1
slow neutrons	3

Melting and boiling points of materials

Material	Melting point in °C	Boiling point in °C
Alcohol	–98	65
Aluminium	660	2470
Copper	1077	2567
Glycerol	18	290
Lead	328	1737
Iron	1537	2737

Specific heat capacity of materials

Material	Specific heat capacity in $J\,kg^{-1}\,°C^{-1}$
Alcohol	2350
Aluminium	902
Copper	386
Glass	500
Ice	2100
Iron	480
Lead	128
Oil	2130
Water	4180

Specific latent heat of fusion of materials

Material	Specific latent heat of fusion in $J\,kg^{-1}$
Alcohol	0.99×10^5
Aluminium	3.95×10^5
Carbon dioxide	1.80×10^5
Copper	2.05×10^5
Iron	2.67×10^5
Lead	0.25×10^5
Water	3.34×10^5

Specific latent heat of vaporisation of materials

Material	Specific latent heat of vaporisation in $J\,kg^{-1}$
Alcohol	11.20×10^5
Carbon dioxide	3.77×10^5
Glycerol	8.30×10^5
Turpentine	2.90×10^5
Water	22.6×10^5

Introduction to Physics

Unit 1   Electricity and Energy

Conservation of energy

Energy transfer and conservation

1. (a) What is the symbol that is used for all types of **energy**?

    (b) What is the unit of energy, and its abbreviation?

2. Name the types of energy involved in each of the following situations.

    (a) The energy associated with the fuel used by a vehicle.

    (b) The energy a vehicle has because of its movement.

    (c) The energy a vehicle gains when it goes up a hill.

    (d) The energy that is produced whenever a force of friction is present.

3. What is meant by an **energy transfer**?

4. Describe the main energy transfer in each of the following situations.

    (a) A car moving off from stationary.

    (b) A car braking to a halt.

    (c) A car going uphill at a constant speed.

    (d) A car going downhill at a constant speed.

5. A sign on a factory wall states:
    "Conservation of energy is important in this building."

    (a) What is meant by **conservation of energy**?

    (b) Explain why it is important to conserve energy.

6. Give **three** ways of conserving energy:

    (a) in the house;

    (b) in transport.

7. State the **principle of conservation of energy**.

8. A student says: "When a ball rolls down a hill the ball loses energy."
    Explain why this statement is **not** true.

Potential and kinetic energy

1. (a) State the relationship that is used to calculate **gravitational potential energy**. Use the symbol for each quantity in the expression.

   (b) What is the quantity corresponding to each symbol?

   (c) What is the unit of each quantity, and its abbreviation?

2. A 52 kg bag of rubble is raised 1.5 m on to the back of a lorry.

   Calculate the potential energy gained by the bag of rubble.

3. A skier has a total mass of 105 kg. The skier starts from rest on a slope at a height of 250 m. The skier travels down the slope and then back up the next slope to come to rest at a height of 75 m.

   Calculate the loss in potential energy as a result of the run.

4. Four tonnes of water every second are allowed to fall through a height of 50 m from behind a dam in a hydro-electric power scheme.

   Calculate the energy available every second from this water.

   (1 tonne = 1000 kg)

5. What type of energy does an object have because of its motion?

6. Copy and complete the following sentence.

   The greater the —————— and/or the greater the —————— of a moving object, the greater is its kinetic energy.

7. (a) State the relationship between **kinetic energy**, **mass** and **speed**. Use the symbol for each quantity in the expression.

   (b) What is the unit of each quantity, and its abbreviation?

8. Calculate the kinetic energy of a trolley of mass 0.75 kg when it is travelling at 2.0 m s^{-1}.

9. A car of mass 800 kg is travelling at 26 m s^{-1} (about 60 mph).
   A lorry of mass 3000 kg is travelling at 13 m s^{-1} (about 30 mph).

   Show by calculation which vehicle has the greater kinetic energy.

10. A child has a mass of 38 kg. The child sits at the top of a chute at a height of 5.0 m. On sliding down, the speed of the child at the bottom is 5.5 ms^{-1}.

    Calculate the energy transferred by friction.

11. Show that, if air resistance can be ignored, the speed of a falling object is independent of its mass and depends only on the height through which it falls.

12. A stone falls from a cliff which is 80 m high.

    (a) If air resistance can be ignored, calculate the speed at which the stone enters the water at the bottom of the cliff.

    (b) What effect will air resistance have on the speed of the stone as it enters the water?

    (c) In practice, not all of the initial potential energy is transferred into kinetic energy.

    Other than kinetic energy, what is the main form of energy produced?

Electrical charge carriers and electric fields

Electrical charge and electrical current

1. What is the difference between an **electrical conductor** and an **insulator**?

2. (a) Give **three** examples of materials that are electrical conductors.

   (b) Give **three** examples of materials that are electrical insulators.

3. Name each of the two types of **electrical charge**.

4. Explain why most objects are normally uncharged.

5. (a) Describe a way to make a plastic rod become charged.

   (b) Explain why the rod becomes charged.

6. Write a statement about:
   (a) the attraction of charges;
   (b) the repulsion of charges.

7. Which kind of charge is carried on an **electron**?

8. (a) What is the symbol for charge?

   (b) What is the unit of charge, and its abbreviation?

9. What is an **electrical current**?

10. (a) What is the symbol for current?

    (b) What is the unit of current, and its abbreviation?

11. State the relationship between **charge**, **current** and **time**.
    Use the symbol for each quantity in the expression.

12. Calculate the current in a circuit when a charge of 180 C is transferred in 1 minute.

13. Calculate the charge transferred in a circuit that has a current of 0.25 A for 1 hour.

14. A capacitor stores 20 mC of charge.
    During discharge there is an average current of 0.5 µA.

    Calculate the time taken to discharge the capacitor.

Alternating and direct current

1. State what is meant by:

   (a) an **alternating current** (a.c.);

   (b) a **direct current** (d.c.).

2. What is the purpose of the mains supply or a battery in an electrical circuit?

3. State which of the two types of electricity, a.c. or d.c., is supplied by:

   (a) the mains supply;

   (b) a battery.

4. Draw the pattern that would be seen on a suitably adjusted oscilloscope when it is connected to:

   (a) a source obtained from the mains supply;

   (b) a battery.

Electric fields

1. What is an **electric field**?

2. What effect does an electric field have on charges?

3. (a) Describe a way to represent an electric field in a diagram.

    (b) Describe a way to represent the strength of an electric field in a diagram.

    (c) (i) Describe a way to represent the direction of an electric field.

      (ii) What is the convention normally used?

4. (a) Draw a diagram to represent an electric field around a positive point charge.

    (b) What term is used to describe the field?

5. (a) Draw a diagram to represent an electric field between two parallel charged plates.

    (b) What term is used to describe the field?

6. What happens to free electric charges in a conductor when an electric field is applied to the conductor?

7. (a) What happens to a charged particle moving parallel to a uniform electric field?

    (b) What happens to a charged particle that enters a uniform electric field while moving initially at right angles to the field?

Potential difference (voltage)

1. What is meant by **potential difference (voltage)**?

2. (a) What is the symbol for **potential difference (voltage)**?

    (b) What is the unit of potential difference (voltage), and its abbreviation?

3. What happens to the brightness of a lamp when the potential difference across it is increased?

4. Two quantities in electricity that are often confused are **voltage** and **current**.

    Show that you understand the differences between these quantities by explaining what is meant by each of them.

Ohm's law

Resistance

1. What is meant by the **electrical resistance** of a resistor?

2. What energy transfer takes place in a resistor?

3. (a) What is the symbol for **resistance**?

   (b) What is the unit of resistance, and its abbreviation?

4. State what happens to the current in a circuit when the resistance in it is increased.

5. (a) State the relationship between **potential difference (voltage), current** and **resistance**.
   Use the symbol for each quantity in the expression.

   (b) What is the unit of each quantity, and its abbreviation?

6. Describe a way to show the relationship between resistance, current and voltage in a simple circuit.
   Your description should include:
   the circuit diagram(s);
   the steps taken to show the relationship.

7. A student sets up the circuit shown to measure the resistance of resistor R. The following results are obtained.

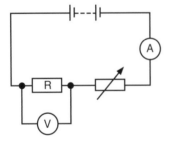

Reading on voltmeter (V)	Reading on ammeter (mA)
0.7	13
1.4	25
2.8	50
4.2	75
5.6	100

(a) Describe the way that the circuit is used to give the set of results.

(b) Plot a graph of the voltmeter readings against the ammeter readings for these results.

(c) Use the graph to determine the resistance of resistor R.

8. State Ohm's law for a conductor.

9. (a) What name is given to the ratio V/I for a resistor?

   (b) What happens to the ratio V/I for a resistor when the current in the resistor changes?

10. (a) What is an ohmic conductor?

    (b) Give the names of **two** ohmic conductors.

11. (a) What is a non-ohmic conductor?

    (b) Give the names of **two** non-ohmic conductors.

12. State the relationship between the **temperature** and the **resistance** of a conductor.

Calculations

1. A student sets up the circuit shown to investigate the resistance of a filament
    lamp. The following results are obtained.

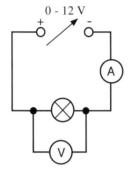

0 - 12 V

Reading on voltmeter (V)	Reading on ammeter (A)	Resistance of lamp (Ω)
0.5	0.10	
1.0	0.20	
2.0	0.38	
3.0	0.44	
5.0	0.49	
7.0	0.51	

(a) (i)   Plot a graph of the voltmeter readings against the ammeter readings
          for the results.

(ii) Use the graph to determine the ammeter reading when the potential
      difference across the lamp is 4.0 V.

(b) Complete the table to show the resistance of the lamp for the different
     meter readings.

(c) (i)   In what way does the resistance of the lamp change as the current
          increases?

(ii) Explain your answer.

2. A car headlight lamp is connected across a 12 V car battery.
    The current in the lamp is 3 A.

    Calculate the resistance of the lamp.

3. A resistor of resistance 180 Ω is connected across a 9 V battery.

    Calculate the current in the resistor.

4. Calculate the potential difference across a 1 kΩ resistor when the current in it is
    10 mA.

5. Calculate the resistance of resistor R in the circuit shown, from the information given.

Reading on voltmeter = 9.0 V
Reading on ammeter = 50 mA

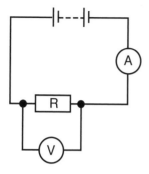

Practical electrical and electronic circuits

Current, voltage and resistance in circuits

1. (a) Name the type of meter used to measure:

      (i)   current;

      (ii) voltage;

      (iii) resistance.

    (b) Draw the circuit symbol for each of the **three** meters.

2. Draw a diagram to show the way that:

    (a) an ammeter is connected into a circuit;

    (b) a voltmeter is connected into a circuit;

    (c) an ohmmeter is used.

3. Redraw the following circuit to include:

    (a) a meter to measure the current in the resistor R;

    (b) a meter to measure the potential difference across the resistor R.

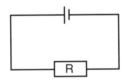

4. Redraw the following circuit to include a meter to measure the current in
    resistor R_1 and a meter to measure the potential difference across resistor R_3.

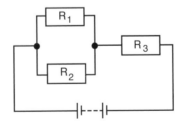

Electrical and electronic components

1. Draw the circuit symbol for:

    (a) (i)   a cell;   (ii)   a battery;

         (iii) a lamp;   (iv)   a switch;

         (v)   a resistor;   (vi)   a fuse.

    (b) State the purpose of each of the **six** components.

2. Starting at the source of energy and working clockwise, name the components in each of the following circuits.

    (a)    (b)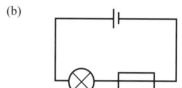

3. (a) What is the purpose of a **variable resistor** in a circuit?

    (b) Draw the circuit symbol for a variable resistor.

    (c) Give **two** practical uses for a variable resistor.

4. Name **two** electrical components that have a resistance that changes due to a change in the physical conditions.

5. (a) What is the purpose of a **motor** in a circuit?

    (b) Draw the circuit symbol for a motor.

6. (a) What is a **diode**?

    (b) Draw the circuit symbol for a diode.

7. (a) What does **LED** stand for?

    (b) Draw the circuit symbol for an LED.

    (c) Indicate the direction that electrons flow in an LED as it emits light.

    (d) Give a use for an LED.

8. An LED is connected in a circuit and it emits light.

    What happens when the connections to the LED are then reversed?

9. Explain why a resistor is needed in series with an LED.

10. Draw a diagram of a circuit that will allow an LED to light.
Include the series resistor and make sure the LED is connected in the correct way to the supply.

11. An LED is used in a circuit with a 12 V supply. The potential difference across the LED is 2 V and the current in it is 10 mA.

Calculate the value of the resistor that is connected in series with the LED.

12. (a) Draw the circuit symbol for a **microphone**.
    (b) State the energy transfer taking place in a microphone.

13. (a) Draw the circuit symbol for a **loudspeaker**.
    (b) State the energy transfer taking place in a loudspeaker.

14. (a) Draw the circuit symbol for a **photovoltaic cell**.
    (b) State the energy transfer taking place in a photovoltaic cell.
    (c) Give **two** uses for a photovoltaic cell.

15. (a) What is the origin of the name '**thermistor**'?
    (b) What is a thermistor?
    (c) Draw the circuit symbol for a thermistor.
    (d) Give a use for a thermistor.

16. A thermistor has a resistance of 30 Ω when hot.
The potential difference across it is 9 V.

Calculate the current in the thermistor.

17. (a) What does **LDR** stand for?
    (b) What is an LDR?
    (c) Draw the circuit symbol for an LDR.
    (d) Give **two** uses for an LDR.

18. An LDR has a current of 10 mA in it and a potential difference of 4 V across it.
Calculate the resistance of the LDR.

19. (a) Draw the circuit symbol for a **relay**.
    (b) Give a use for a relay.

20. (a) What is the purpose of a **capacitor** in an electronic circuit?

    (b) Draw the circuit symbol for a capacitor.

21. (a) Draw a circuit that could be used to charge a capacitor.

    (b) What happens to the potential difference across a capacitor during the time it is charging?

    (c) Sketch a graph of the potential difference across a capacitor during the time it is charging.

22. A capacitor is connected across a 9 V battery.

    (a) When does the capacitor stop charging?

    (b) What does the time taken to charge a capacitor depend on?

23. A capacitor is fully charged when the potential difference across it is the same as the supply voltage.

    In what way could the time taken to fully charge this capacitor be reduced, using the same supply voltage?

24. In what way can a charged capacitor be quickly discharged?

25. Draw the circuit symbol, labelling the terminals, for

    (a) an **npn transistor** (bipolar transistor);

    (b) an **n-channel enhancement mode MOSFET**.

26. (a) Give a use for a transistor.

    (b) "A transistor has two possible states – it can be ON or OFF."

    Explain what is meant by this statement.

Series and parallel circuits

1. (a) What is meant by a **series circuit**?

   (b) Draw a circuit diagram showing a resistor and a lamp in a series circuit with a cell.

2. Write a statement about the current at all points in a series circuit.

3. State the relationship between the voltage of the supply and the voltages across the components in a series circuit.

4. By considering the relationship between the voltage of the supply and the voltages across the components in a series circuit, show that the law of conservation of energy applies.

5. In the circuit shown, all of the resistors are identical.

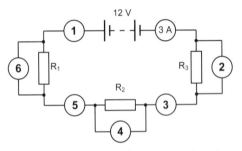

   State the value, with units, on each of the meters **1** to **6**.

6. Give an application in the home that uses **two** switches in series.

7. (a) What is meant by a **parallel circuit**?

   (b) Draw a circuit diagram with a cell showing two resistors, R_1 and R_2, in parallel.

8. State the relationship between the current drawn from the supply and the currents in parallel branches in a parallel circuit.

9. Write a statement about the voltage across resistors connected in a parallel circuit.

10. In the circuit shown all of the lamps are identical.

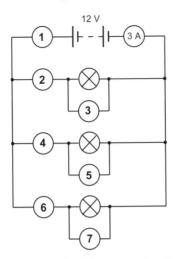

12 V

State the value, with units, on each of the meters **1** to **7**.

11. Explain why connecting too many household appliances to one electrical socket is dangerous.

12. Draw a circuit diagram to show the way that all four car sidelights are connected to the car battery.

13. Draw a circuit diagram to show the way that the two headlights in a car can only be switched on when the ignition switch and the light switch are both on.

14. Car brakelights only go on when the ignition is switched on and the brake switch is pressed.

    Draw the circuit diagram for this arrangement.

15. The interior light in a car goes on when either the driver's door or the passenger's door is opened.

    (a) What happens to the door switch when a door is opened?

    (b) Draw the circuit diagram used to switch the light on.

16. State what is meant by:

    (a) an **open circuit**;

    (b) a **short circuit**.

17. (a) Describe how to make a simple continuity tester using a battery and a lamp. Include a diagram of the circuit used in your description.

    (b) Describe how this continuity tester can be used to test for faults in a circuit.

18. State the reading on an ohmmeter when it is placed across:

    (a) an open circuit;

    (b) a short circuit.

19. (a) Are appliances connected in series or in parallel when they are connected to the mains through the wiring of a house?

    (b) Is the lighting circuit in a house a series circuit or a parallel circuit?

20. (a) Describe what is meant by a ring main circuit. Use a circuit diagram to help your description.

    (b) What are the advantages of using a ring main circuit instead of a simple parallel circuit?

    (c) Give **two** differences between the lighting circuit and the ring main circuit in the wiring of a house.

21. (a) What is the purpose of the mains fuses in the mains wiring of a house?

    (b) Explain the way that the mains fuses do the job that they are designed to do.

22. (a) Explain why more than one mains fuse is necessary in the mains wiring of a house.

    (b) Explain why different values of mains fuses are required in the mains wiring of a house.

Resistors in circuits

1. (a) Draw a diagram showing **three** resistors R_1, R_2 and R_3 in series.

    (b) State the relationship between the resistances R_1, R_2 and R_3 and R_T, the total resistance.

    (c) What happens to the total resistance of a circuit when resistors are connected in series?

2. Calculate the total resistance of each of the following combinations.

    (a)

    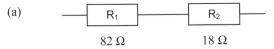

    82 Ω   18 Ω

    (b)

    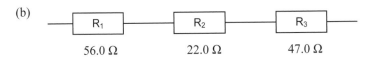

    56.0 Ω   22.0 Ω   47.0 Ω

3. Three resistors of values 2.20 Ω, 4.70 Ω and 5.60 Ω are connected in series. Calculate the total resistance of this combination.

4. (a) Draw a diagram showing **three** resistors R_1, R_2 and R_3 in parallel.

    (b) State the relationship between the resistances R_1, R_2 and R_3 and R_T, the total resistance.

    (c) What happens to the total resistance of a circuit when resistors are connected in parallel?

5. Calculate the total resistance of each of the following combinations.

    (a)

    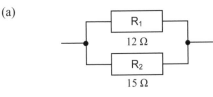

    (b)

    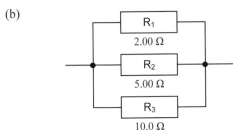

6. Resistors of values 10 Ω, 12 Ω and 15 Ω are connected in parallel. Calculate the total resistance of this combination.

7. Calculate the total resistance between points **A** and **B** in the circuit shown.

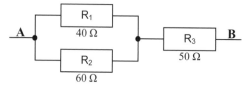

Potential divider circuits

1. (a) What is a **potential divider circuit**?

    (b) What is the purpose of the resistor R in the circuit shown?

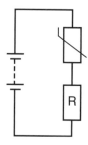

2. Consider the potential divider circuit shown.

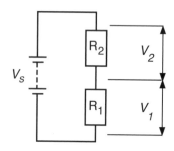

    (a) State the relationship between V_1, V_2, R_1 and R_2.

    (b) State the relationship between V_S, V_1 and V_2, and use this to find the relationship for V_1 in terms of V_S, R_1 and R_2.

3. Calculate the potential difference V_1
    in the potential divider circuit shown.

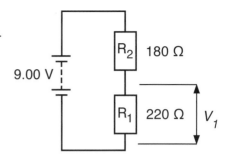

4. A potential divider consists of a resistor R_1 of value 1000 Ω in series with a
    resistor R_2 of value 1500 Ω. It is connected across a supply voltage of 2.5 V.

    (a) Draw the circuit diagram.

    (b) Calculate the voltage across R_1.

5. A potential divider consisting of two resistors is used to 'tap off' exactly half of
    a supply voltage.

    What is the relationship between the resistances of the two resistors?

Electronic systems and circuits

1. (a) What is meant by an **output device** in an electronic system?

   (b) What is meant by an **input device** in an electronic system?

2. State the output energy for each of the following output devices:

   (a) an LED; (b) a loudspeaker;

   (c) a motor; (d) a relay.

3. Name a suitable output device for each of the following applications.

   (a) A system to turn a conveyor belt round in a bottling factory.

   (b) As an audible warning when an incubator has become too cold.

   (c) A stereo hi-fi system.

   (d) As a 'power-on' indicator for an MP4 player.

   (e) To switch on a high current electric motor by using a small current.

4. For each of the applications given, choose a suitable input device from the following list:
   microphone; photovoltaic cell; thermistor; LDR; capacitor.

   (a) An energy source for a satellite.

   (b) A time delay before arming a burglar alarm to allow the householder out of the front door.

   (c) A temperature control for an aquarium.

   (d) An alarm to warn parents in another room when a baby wakes up and cries.

   (e) A circuit to turn down the brightness of a television when the room lights are put out.

5. Name a suitable input device for each of the following applications.

   (a) A coin detector in a drinks machine.

   (b) A fog detector.

   (c) A heartbeat monitor.

   (d) A circuit to switch a hand drier on for 10 s.

   (e) A flame sensor for a gas fire.

6. Consider each of the following circuits.

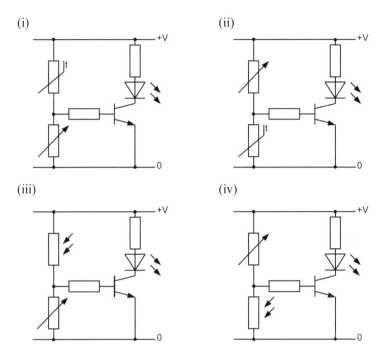

(i)   (ii)

(iii)   (iv)

(a) What does each of the circuits do?

(b) Explain the way that each of the circuits operates.

(c) What is the purpose of the variable resistor in the circuits?

7. A circuit similar to the one shown below can be used as an egg timer, lighting an LED after a set time period.

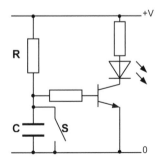

Explain how the circuit works, in particular mentioning the function of components **S**, **R**, **C** and the transistor.

Electricity and Energy

Electrical power

Household appliances

1. What is the job done by all electrical appliances?

2. (a) Describe the main energy transformation in each of the following household appliances:
   toaster; table lamp; kettle; vacuum cleaner; electric fire.

   (b) In which part of an electric fire does the energy transfer take place?

3. (a) Explain what is meant by the power rating of a household appliance.

   (b) What is the unit that is used to measure the power rating of an appliance, and its abbreviation?

   (c) What information is usually given on the rating plate of a mains-operated appliance?

4. (a) Give the approximate power rating of each of the following household appliances:
   toaster; hair dryer; kettle; light bulb; electric fire; shaver; cooker.

   (b) As a very general rule, which type of household appliance has the highest power rating?

5. (a) What is the purpose of the flexible cable (flex) attached to a household appliance?

   (b) What factor is used to decide the size of flex?

   (c) Explain what can happen if too thin a flex is used.

6. (a) What is the purpose of the fuse in a plug?

   (b) Explain the way that a fuse does the job that it is designed to do.

7. (a) State the **two** values of fuse recommended for use in household plugs.

   (b) Explain the way to choose the correct fuse to use in the plug of a household appliance, when the power rating of the appliance is known.

   (c) Explain the way to choose the correct fuse to fit in the plug of a household appliance, when the current taken by the appliance is known or can be calculated.

8. Explain why some household appliances, such as vacuum cleaners, which have electric motors, may need a 13 A fuse even although their constant power rating is less than 700 W.

Power, energy and time

1. (a) What is the symbol for energy?

   (b) What is the unit of energy, and its abbreviation?

2. Explain what is meant by power.

3. (a) What is the symbol for power?

   (b) What is the unit of power, and its abbreviation?

   (c) State the relationship between the unit of power and the joule.

4. State the relationship between **power**, **energy** and **time**.
   Use the symbol for each quantity in the expression.

5. Calculate the energy transferred in a 150 W lamp every minute.

6. (a) What is a kilowatt-hour?

   (b) State how to calculate the energy transferred in kilowatt-hours, given the power of an appliance and the time in use.

   (c) Calculate the number of kilowatt-hours used by a 5.00 kW electric fire that is switched on for 2 hours 15 minutes.

7. Complete a calculation to show the way that the two units, the **kilowatt-hour** and the **joule** are related.

8. (a) Calculate the number of kilowatt-hours of energy that are wasted if 1000 people each leave one 100 W lamp on unnecessarily for 1 hour.

   (b) Calculate the cost of this wasted energy if each kilowatt-hour costs 10 p.

   (c) If each lamp is only 10% efficient, calculate the number of kilowatt-hours of electricity that need to be generated unnecessarily.

Power, voltage, current and resistance in electrical circuits

1. Using the symbol for each quantity in the expression, state the relationship between:

    (a) **power**, **voltage** and **current**;

    (b) **power**, **current** and **resistance**;

    (c) **power**, **voltage** and **resistance**.

2. VI, I^2R and $\dfrac{V^2}{R}$ are used to calculate electrical power.

    Show that they are equal to each other.

3. Explain why the heating element of an electric fire gets hot while the flex, which connects the fire to the mains, does not.

4. Explain what happens to the brightness of a lamp when the current in it is increased.

5. Each of the appliances in the table is connected to a 230 V mains.

Appliance	Power (W)	Current (A)
Microwave oven	1380	
Bedside lamp	100	
Sandwich maker	920	
Television	300	

    (a) Calculate the current in each of the appliances.

    (b) (i) Use the current in the microwave oven to determine the value of the fuse to fit in the plug.

    (ii) Use the current in the bedside lamp to explain why the lamp should have a 3 A fuse fitted in the plug.

6. A car headlight is connected to a 12 V car battery.
   The current in the lamp is 3.0 A.

    Calculate the power rating of the lamp.

7. A 690 W television is connected to a 230 V supply.

    Calculate the current in the television.

8. Calculate the electrical energy transferred into other forms of energy every second in a 10 kΩ resistor when the current in it is 5.0 mA.

9. There is a current of 0.25 A in a 60 W lamp.

   Calculate the resistance of the lamp.

10. The input voltage of an amplifier is 10 mV and its input resistance is 10 kΩ.

    Calculate the input power of the amplifier.

11. There is a current of 0.25 A in a torch lamp when operated from a 3.0 V battery.

    Calculate the power rating of the lamp.

12. A car sidelight lamp is marked 5.0 W, 12 V.

    Calculate the resistance of the filament of the lamp.

13. A floodlight lamp with a resistance of 92 Ω is connected to the 230 V mains supply.

    (a) Calculate the current in the lamp.

    (b) Use this current to determine the value of the fuse required for the lamp.

Specific heat capacity

Temperature and heat energy

1. (a) What is a **thermometer**?

   (b) What do all thermometers have in common?

2. (a) Name **four** different types of thermometer.

   (b) For each type, give the physical property that changes with temperature.

3. Describe the way that a liquid in glass thermometer operates.
   Include a labelled diagram in your description.

4. What is meant by the **temperature** of an object?

5. Name **two** scales (apart from Fahrenheit) used to measure temperature.

6. Copy and complete the following sentence.

   As the temperature of a gas increases, the mean (average) kinetic energy of its particles ———— and they move ————.

7. Copy and complete the following sentences.

   (a) ———— is a measure of how hot or cold an object is.
   It is usually measured in ———— ————.

   (b) Heat is a form of ———— and is measured in ————.

   (c) Putting ———— energy into an object usually makes its ————
   increase.

8. Copy and complete the following sentence.

   Heat energy travels from a region of ———— temperature to a region of ———— temperature.

9. What does loss of heat energy in a given time depend upon?

Calculations

1. (a) Does 1 kg of copper need the same heat energy as 1 kg of aluminium to raise its temperature by 1 °C?

    (b) Explain your answer.

2. (a) Compare the heat energy needed to raise the temperature of 2 kg of water by 1 °C with that needed to do the same to 1 kg of water.

    (b) Explain your answer.

3. (a) Compare the heat energy needed to raise the temperature of 1 kg of copper by 1 °C with that needed to raise the temperature by 2 °C.

    (b) Explain your answer.

4. (a) Compare the heat energy needed to raise the temperature of 1 kg of copper from 9 °C to 10 °C with that needed to raise the temperature from 99 °C to 100 °C.

    (b) Explain your answer.

5. What is meant by the **specific heat capacity** of a substance?

6. (a) State the equation that links **heat energy** to the **mass, specific heat capacity** and **temperature change** of a substance.
    Use the symbol for each quantity in the expression.

    (b) What is the unit of each quantity, and its abbreviation?

7. Calculate the heat energy needed to increase the temperature of 1.00 kg of aluminium by 10.0 °C.

8. Calculate the heat energy needed to raise the temperature of 2.00 kg of water from 20.0 °C to 90.0 °C.

9. A student calculated that 2.2×10^2 kJ of heat energy is required to bring water in a metal can to its boiling point. In practice, the actual heat energy required is greater.

    Give a reason for this difference.

10. There is 5.0 kg of coolant in the cooling system of a car.
    The coolant absorbs 720 kJ of energy from the car engine.

    Calculate the increase in temperature of the coolant.

    (The specific heat capacity of the coolant used is 2400 J kg^{-1} °C^{-1}.)

11. An electric kettle is rated at 2.2 kW and has a capacity of 1.5 litres of water.

Calculate the time it takes to increase the temperature of the water from room temperature (20 °C) to boiling point, without boiling any water off. Assume that all the energy from the kettle goes into the water.

(Mass of 1 litre of water = 1.0 kg)

12. (a) State the **principle of conservation of energy**.

(b) A car of mass 1000 kg, travelling at 4.0 m s^{-1}, is brought to rest by applying the brakes.

Calculate the increase in temperature of the brake linings and pads if all of The original kinetic energy of the car is transformed to heat energy in the brakes.

(Total mass of brake lining material = 0.5 kg;
specific heat capacity of brake lining material = 500 J kg^{-1} °C^{-1})

Gas laws and the kinetic model

Pressure

1. What is the definition of **pressure**?

2. (a) What is the symbol that is used for pressure?

    (b) What is the SI unit of pressure, and its abbreviation?

3. There is another unit that is used for pressure, derived from the definition of pressure.

    What is this unit, and its abbreviation?

4. (a) State the relationship between **pressure** (p), **force** (F) and **unit area** (A).

    (b) What is the unit of each quantity, and its abbreviation?

5. An elephant weighs 5900 N and the total area of all four of its feet is 0.08 m^2.

    Calculate the pressure exerted on the ground by the elephant when it is standing on all four feet.

6. A student weighs 500 N.

    Calculate the pressure on the floor when standing on one heel of area of 1 cm^2 (1 x 10^{-4} m^2).

7. Explain the way that snow shoes, which have a large area, stop the wearer sinking into soft snow.

8. Explain why it is easier to cut vegetables with a sharp knife compared to a blunt knife.

The kinetic model

1. (a) Describe what is meant by **Brownian motion**.

   (b) According to the kinetic model, matter consists of particles that are in constant motion.

   Explain the way that Brownian motion provides evidence for this theory.

2. Copy and complete the following sentences using words or phrases chosen from the list below:
   gas; liquid; particles; solid; close together; free to move; very fast; very far apart; vibrating slowly.

   (You will have to use some words more than once and sometimes use the plural of the word.)

   (a) The kinetic model of matter describes how ——————, ——————
   and —————— behave by considering how the ——————
   that make up matter are arranged and move.

   (b) In a ——————, the —————— are closely packed, ——————
   about fixed positions in ordered rows.

   (c) In a ——————, the —————— are also —————— but are
   —————— anywhere in the material.

   (d) In a ——————, the —————— are —————— and move ——————
   in all directions.

   (e) The —————— of a —————— completely fill all the space of the container.

3. The kinetic model of a gas describes a gas in terms of particles.

   (a) Describe how the particles make up a gas by considering their number, their spacing and their movement (direction and speed).

   (b) Explain what is meant by the volume of a gas by considering the container of the gas and the volume of the individual particles.

   (c) What is happening when the particles of a gas affect each other?

   (d) Describe the change in speed and average kinetic energy of the particles as the temperature changes.

4. The kinetic model accounts for the pressure of a gas.

   (a) What happens when the particles of a gas collide with the walls of the container?

   (b) Use your answer to part (a) to state what is meant by the pressure of a gas.

   (c) In terms of the particles, what would cause the pressure of the gas to increase?

The gas laws: volume and pressure

1. State the relationship between the **pressure** (p), and the **volume** (V) of a fixed mass of gas at constant temperature.

2. Describe an experiment to show the relationship between the pressure and volume of a fixed mass of gas at constant temperature.

3. (a) Sketch a graph of pressure against volume of a fixed mass of gas at constant temperature.

   (b) Sketch a graph of pressure against 1/volume of a fixed mass of gas at constant temperature.

4. State the **pressure-volume law (Boyle's Law)** in words.

5. A fixed mass of gas at a pressure p_1 with a volume V_1 has its pressure and volume changed to p_2 and V_2 respectively, without a change in temperature.

   (a) State the relationship between p_1, V_1, p_2 and V_2.

   (b) In completing calculations using this relationship, what must be kept in mind with respect to the units?

6. A scuba gas tank contains 2 litres of air at a pressure of 5×10^5 Pa.

   Calculate the volume of this air at atmospheric pressure (1×10^5 Pa), if the temperature does not change.

7. A flask contains 1 litre of air at a pressure of 1 atmosphere (1×10^5 Pa). A syringe is attached to the flask and used to add an extra 10 ml of air to the flask without a change in temperature.

   Calculate the pressure of the air now in the flask.

8. Use the kinetic model of a gas to explain the decrease in pressure when the volume of a gas increases without a change in temperature.

Different temperature scales

1. (a) What temperature on the Celsius scale is known as absolute zero?

   (b) What is this temperature on the absolute scale of temperature?

   (c) What is the unit of temperature used on the absolute scale of temperature, and its abbreviation?

2. (a) What is, theoretically, the lowest temperature that can be reached by any substance?

   (b) Explain why temperatures lower than this value cannot be reached.

3. (a) What is the way to convert a temperature reading on the Celsius scale into a reading on the absolute scale?

   (b) What is the way to convert a temperature reading on the absolute scale into a reading on the Celsius scale?

4. (a) Convert each of the following temperatures on the Celsius scale into a kelvin temperature.

   (i)   -273 °C   (ii) 27 °C   (iii) 100 °C

   (b) Convert each of the following kelvin temperatures into a Celsius temperature.

   (i)   0 K   (ii) 273 K   (iii) 400 K

5. Compare the size of one degree Celsius with one kelvin.

6. The temperature of a gas increases by 50 °C.

   What is this temperature increase expressed in kelvins?

The gas laws: pressure and temperature

1. (a) State the relationship between the **pressure** (p), and the **temperature** (T) of a fixed mass of gas at constant volume.

   (b) What scale of temperature must be used with this relationship?

2. Describe an experiment to show the relationship between the pressure and temperature of a fixed mass of gas at constant volume.

3. (a) Sketch a graph of pressure against temperature in degrees Celsius for a fixed mass of gas at constant volume.

   (b) Sketch a graph of pressure against temperature in kelvins for a fixed mass of gas at constant volume.

4. State the **pressure-temperature law (The Pressure Law)** in words.

5. A fixed mass of gas originally at a pressure p_1 and temperature T_1, has its pressure and temperature changed to p_2 and T_2 respectively, without the volume changing.

   (a) State the relationship between p_1, T_1, p_2 and T_2.

   (b) In completing calculations using this relationship, what must be kept in mind with respect to the units?

6. A car tyre contains air at a pressure of 2.0×10^5 Pa when the temperature is 27 °C. After a long drive, the temperature of the air in the tyre rises to 57 °C, without a change in volume.

   Calculate the new pressure of the air in the tyre.

7. A fixed mass of gas is trapped in a rigid container at a pressure of 1 atmosphere (1×10^5 Pa). The kelvin temperature of the gas is doubled.

   Calculate the new pressure of the gas in the container, in Pa.

8. Use the kinetic model of a gas to explain the increase in pressure when the temperature of a gas increases without a change in volume.

The gas laws: volume and temperature

1. (a) State the relationship between the **volume** (V), and the **temperature** (T) of a fixed mass of gas at constant pressure.

    (b) What scale of temperature must be used with this relationship?

2. Describe an experiment to show the relationship between the volume and the temperature of a fixed mass of gas at constant pressure.

3. (a) Sketch a graph of volume against temperature in degrees Celsius of a fixed mass of gas at constant pressure.

    (b) Sketch a graph of volume against temperature in kelvins for a fixed mass of gas at constant pressure.

4. State the **volume-temperature law (Charles' Law)** in words.

5. A fixed mass of gas with an original volume V_1 and temperature T_1, has its volume and temperature changed to V_2 and T_2 respectively, without the pressure changing.

    (a) State the relationship between V_1, T_1, V_2 and T_2.

    (b) In completing calculations using this relationship, what must be kept in mind with respect to the units?

6. A fixed mass of air is contained in a cylinder that has a heater and a freely moving piston.

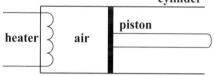

    At a temperature of 27 °C, the volume of air in the cylinder is 0.10 m³.
    The heater is switched on and the temperature of the air increases to 177 °C.

    Calculate the new volume of air in the cylinder.

7. The gas in a closed balloon only occupies 90% of the maximum volume of the balloon at a temperature of -3 °C.

    Calculate the temperature the gas in the balloon has to be increased to so that it occupies the maximum volume of the balloon without a change in pressure.

8. Use the kinetic model of a gas to explain the increase in volume when the pressure of a gas increases without a change in temperature.

The gas laws: the combined gas equation

1. State the relationship between the **pressure** (p), the **volume** (V) and the **absolute temperature** (T) of a fixed mass of gas **(The Combined Gas Equation)**.

2. A fixed mass of gas has original pressure, volume and absolute temperature values of p_1, V_1 and T_1 respectively. These values are changed to p_2, V_2 and T_2.

    State the relationship between these six quantities.

3. A weather balloon contains 6.0 m^3 of helium at a pressure of 1.0 x 10^5 Pa and a temperature of 27 °C. After launch, the pressure increases to 5.5 x 10^5 Pa and the temperature falls to -23 °C.

    Calculate the new volume of the gas in the balloon.

Wave parameters and behaviours

Waves and energy

1. What is meant by a **wave**?

2. Copy and complete the following sentence.

   Waves transfer —————— from one place to another; they are created by —————— .

3. Sound is carried by means of waves.
   Give the names of **three** other types of waves.

Wave parameters

1. (a) What is the difference between a **transverse wave** and a **longitudinal wave**?
   (b) Give an example of a transverse wave.
   (c) Give an example of a longitudinal wave.

2. (a) What is meant by the **frequency** of a wave?
   (b) What is the symbol that is used for frequency?
   (c) What is the unit of frequency, and its abbreviation?
   (d) What is the definition of the unit of frequency?

3. (a) What is meant by the **period** of a wave?
   (b) What is the symbol that is used for the period of a wave?
   (c) What is the unit of period, and its abbreviation?

4. (a) What is meant by the **wavelength** of a wave?
   (b) What is the symbol that is used for wavelength?
   (c) What is the unit of wavelength, and its abbreviation?

5. (a) What is meant by the **speed** or **velocity** of a wave?

   (b) What is the symbol that is used for wave speed?

   (c) What is the unit of wave speed, and its abbreviation?

6. (a) What is meant by the **amplitude** of a wave?

   (b) What is the symbol that is used for amplitude?

   (c) What is the unit of amplitude, and its abbreviation?

7. Draw a diagram of a transverse wave.
   On your diagram mark:
   a crest;
   a trough;
   one wavelength;
   the amplitude.

Calculations

1. A tuning fork produces 81 600 vibrations in 4 minutes.

   Calculate the frequency of the wave produced.

2. What is the relationship between **wave period** (*T*) and **wave frequency** (*f*)?

3. A wave generator in a swimming pool produces waves with a frequency of 0.21 Hz.

   Calculate the period of the waves.

4. (a) State the relationship between **distance**, **time** and **speed**.
       Use the symbol for each quantity in the expression.

   (b) What is the unit of each quantity, and its abbreviation?

5. The speed of sound in air is 340 m s^{-1}.

   Calculate how far a sound will travel in 5.0 s.

6. A student uses two sound operated switches, 1.7 m apart, connected to an interface and a computer, to obtain a value for the speed of sound. The computer records a time of 5.0 x 10^{-3} s for sound to travel between the switches.

   Use these results to calculate the speed of sound.

7. During a thunderstorm, a girl notices that the sound of thunder comes 3.00 s after she has seen the flash of lightning.
   The speed of sound in air is 340 m s^{-1}.

   Calculate the distance from the girl to the storm.

8. A lighthouse sends out a flash of light and a burst of sound at the same time. The speed of sound in air is 340 m s^{-1}. An observer on a ship is 1.36 km from the lighthouse.

   Calculate the time interval between the observer seeing the light and hearing the sound.

9. A doctor sends a pulse of sound through a patient's body tissue for diagnosis. The sound takes 0.2 millisecond (0.0002 second) to travel 0.3 m in the body tissue.

   Calculate the speed of sound in the body tissue.

10. The sound of a train takes 0.50 second to travel 2.6 kilometres along the steel railway lines.

    Calculate the speed of sound in steel.

11. Water waves move a distance of 8.8 m in 4.0 s.

    Calculate the speed of the waves.

12. Water waves have a speed of 3.0 m s^{-1}.

    How far do the waves move in 5.0 s?

13. The speed of water waves is 4.0 m s^{-1}.

    Calculate the time taken for the waves to travel 14 m.

14. (a) State the relationship between **speed**, **frequency** and **wavelength**. Use the symbol for each quantity in the expression.

    (b) What is the unit of each quantity, and its abbreviation?

15. A wave generator in a swimming pool has a frequency of 10 Hz. The wavelength of the waves it produces is 0.4 m.

    Calculate the speed of the waves.

16. A tuning fork produces a note with a frequency of 262 Hz.

    Calculate the wavelength of the sound waves produced in air when the wave speed is 340 m s^{-1}.

17. The waves in a harbour have a wavelength of 0.50 m and a speed of 0.25 m s^{-1}. A boat is anchored in the harbour.

    Calculate how many times per second the boat will bob up and down.

18. A transmitter produces microwaves of wavelength 2.8 cm.

    Calculate the frequency of the waves.

19. Show, for a wave, that wave frequency multiplied by wavelength is equal to distance travelled divided by time taken.

Diffraction

1. What is meant by **diffraction** of a wave?

2. Show, using diagrams, whether long wavelength waves or short wavelength waves are diffracted more on passing a barrier.

3. Explain in terms of diffraction the way that wavelength affects radio and television reception.

4. Explain why long waves in the low frequency radio band travel long distances.

5. When waves pass through a gap, the width of the gap determines how much diffraction occurs.

    Using diagrams, describe the waves emerging:

    (a) when the gap is less than or equal to the wavelength of the waves;

    (b) when the gap is greater than the wavelength of the waves.

Electromagnetic spectrum

The bands of the electromagnetic spectrum

1. (a) Name the **seven** bands of radiation that collectively are known as the **electromagnetic spectrum**.

   (b) What do all of these radiations have in common?

   (c) What **two** properties are different for the radiations in this family of waves?

2. (a) Copy and complete the first column in the table to include all **seven** types of radiation in the electromagnetic spectrum.

Type of radiation	Approximate wavelength range (m)	Approximate frequency range (Hz)	Source	Detector
	shortest	highest		
	↑	↑		
	↓	↓		
	longest	lowest		

   (b) Give a typical source for each of the bands of radiation.

   (c) Name a detector for each of the bands of radiation.

3. State the relationship between the frequency and the energy associated with the radiations in the bands of the electromagnetic spectrum.

4. Radio waves, TV waves and microwaves are **invisible** to the naked eye.

   (a) Which is the only type of radiation that is **visible** to the naked eye?

   (b) Name **four** other types of radiation that are **invisible** to the naked eye.

Applications of the electromagnetic spectrum

1. (a) What is a **laser**?

   (b) Where does the name come from?

   (c) Give **three** uses of laser light.

2. A solid-state laser emits light that has a wavelength of 660 nm.
   Calculate the frequency of the light emitted.

3. (a) What is another name for **infrared** radiation?

   (b) Which part of our bodies can detect infrared radiation?

   (c) Give **three** applications of infrared radiation.

4. (a) Why is a low dose of **ultraviolet** radiation beneficial to us?

   (b) Give a use of ultraviolet radiation in the area of:

      (i) medicine;

      (ii) security.

   (c) Why does the use of sun-block products limit the damage to the skin by the Sun?

   (d) Why is there concern about damage being done to the ozone layer?

5. (a) What are **X-rays**?

   (b) Give **two** ways to detect X-rays.

6. X-rays are used in medicine to detect broken bones.

   (a) What happens to the X-rays that meet soft tissue such as skin and muscle?

   (b) What happens to the X-rays that meet dense tissue such as bone?

7. What are X-ray machines used for in airports?

8. (a) Why do we have to be careful about exposure to X-rays?

   (b) Give a precaution that radiographers take when working with X-rays.

   (c) Which types of cell are most harmed by too much exposure to X-rays?

9. What is the source of **gamma rays**?

10. (a) Explain why gamma rays can be used in medicine to sterilise instruments, without affecting the instruments themselves.

    (b) Give another use for gamma rays in medicine.

11. (a) In what form do radio and television signals travel through space?

    (b) What do radio and television signals transfer from place to place?

    (c) What is the speed of radio and television signals through air and space?

12. It takes 1.2 s for a radio signal sent from a beacon on the Moon to be received on Earth.

    Calculate the distance between the Moon and the Earth.

13. BBC Radio 5 Live broadcasts on a frequency of 909 kHz.

    Calculate the wavelength of the radio waves transmitted.

14. The wavelength of the radio waves transmitted by the Forth 2 station is 194 m.

    Calculate the frequency allocated to the Forth 2 radio station.

15. What property of waves in the VHF (very high frequency) waveband makes them unsuitable for long range communication?

16. (a) Give a use for **microwaves**.

    (b) What property of microwaves makes them suitable for satellite communication?

Light

1. (a) What is meant by **refraction** of light?

    (b) Give **two** uses of refraction of light.

2. In relation to a ray of light being refracted on passing from air into glass, state what is meant by;

    (a) the angle of incidence;

    (b) the angle of refraction;

    (c) the normal.

3. A ray of light passes from air into glass (but not along the normal).

    Draw a diagram to show the path of the ray.
    On your diagram, label the following:
          the incident ray;
          the refracted ray;
          the normal;
          the angle of incidence;
          the angle of refraction.

4. Copy and complete the diagram to show the path of the ray of light as it enters and leaves the glass block.

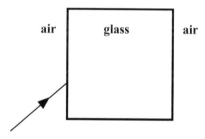

    Label the relevant normals on your diagram.

5. Draw a labelled diagram to explain why a straight stick that is partly submerged in water appears to bend.

6. What happens to wave speed when a wave enters a more dense medium?

7. Copy and complete the following sentences using a word from the list:
   always; never; sometimes.

   (You will have to use one word more than once.)

   (a) When a wave refracts, the wave speed ———— changes.

   (b) When a wave refracts, the frequency ———— changes.

   (c) When a wave refracts, the wavelength ———— changes.

   (d) When a wave refracts, the direction ———— changes.

8. (a) Describe the shape of a **converging (convex)** lens.
       Draw a diagram to help your description.

   (b) Describe the shape of a **diverging (concave)** lens.
       Draw a diagram to help your description.

9. Draw a diagram to show the way that light is refracted by:

   (a) a convex lens;

   (b) a concave lens.

10. (a) Draw a labelled diagram to show what happens when a beam of white light is incident on a triangular prism.

    (b) Why does a triangular prism have this effect on a beam of white light?

Nuclear radiation

The nature of radiation

1. Describe a simple model of an **atom**.
   Include a labelled diagram to help your description.

2. (a) Name the **three** main particles that make up an atom.

   (b) What are the relative masses of each of the particles?

   (c) Where in an atom is most of the mass concentrated?

3. State the type of electrical charge on:

   (a) a proton;

   (b) an electron;

   (c) a neutron.

4. Some **isotopes** are said to be **radioactive**.

   (a) What is meant by isotopes?

   (b) What name is given to isotopes that are radioactive?

   (c) What is meant by 'to be radioactive'?

5. What can happen to the energy that radiation carries when it passes through a material?

6. Name the **three** types of radiation.

7. What is an **alpha particle**?
   In your answer, state its atomic number, mass number and the electrical charge that it carries.

8. What is a **beta particle**?
   In your answer, state its origins, its approximate mass and the electrical charge that it carries.

9. (a) What are **gamma rays**?

   (b) What causes gamma radiation to be emitted from an atom?

10. (a) State the approximate range in air of all **three** types of radiation.

    (b) State the approximate minimum thickness of material that would absorb each of the **three** types of radiation.

11. Which of the three types of radiation is most penetrating to the human body?

12. Why is an atom normally uncharged even although it contains charged particles?

13. When radiation passes through a material it can **ionise** the atoms of that material.

    (a) What is meant by ionisation?

    (b) Which of the three types of radiation produces the greatest ionisation density of atoms?

Dosimetry

1. (a) Explain what is meant by the **activity** of a radioactive source.

   (b) What is the symbol for activity?

   (c) What is the unit of activity, and its abbreviation?

   (d) What is the definition of the unit of activity?

   (e) State the relationship between the **activity** of a radioactive source, the **number of nuclei** that decay (N) and the **period** (t).

2. Why is it acceptable to talk about 'the activity of a sample of uranium' but meaningless to talk about 'the activity of radon'?

3. Why does a 1 g sample of a radioisotope of radium show a different activity from a 1 g sample of radium oxide containing the same radioisotope?

4. A sample of rock has an activity of 21.0 Bq.

   Calculate the number of nuclei that decay every hour.

5. Over a period of 20 s, 8×10^7 atoms of a particular radioactive sample decay.

   Calculate the activity of the sample.

6. (a) Explain what is meant by **absorbed dose**.

   (b) What is the symbol for absorbed dose?

   (c) What is the unit of absorbed dose, and its abbreviation?

   (d) What is the definition of the unit of absorbed dose?

   (e) Using symbols, state the relationship between the **absorbed dose**, the **energy absorbed** (E) and the **mass** of the absorbing material (m).

7. An adult and an infant are exposed to the same amount of energy from a radioactive source.

   Why does the radiation have a greater effect on the infant than on the adult?

8. When a human organ of mass 50 g is exposed to ionising radiation, the absorbed dose is 20 Gy.

   Calculate the energy absorbed by the organ.

9. (a) Explain what is meant by the **radiation weighting factor** for radiation.

   (b) What is the symbol for the radiation weighting factor?

   (c) Why does the radiation weighting factor **not** have a unit?

10. Copy the table below and complete it using information on the Data Sheet.

Type of radiation	Radiation weighting factor
alpha particles (α)	
beta particles (β)	
gamma rays (γ)	
slow (thermal) neutrons	

11. (a) Explain what is meant by **equivalent dose.**

    (b) What is the symbol for equivalent dose?

    (c) What is the unit of equivalent dose, and its abbreviation?

    (d) Using symbols, state the relationship between **equivalent dose, absorbed dose** and the **radiation weighting factor** (w_r).

12. (a) Give **three** factors that can affect the biological impact of radiation.

    (b) Give **two** ways to reduce the biological impact of radiation on a person.

13. (a) Explain what is meant by **equivalent dose rate**.

    (b) What is the symbol for equivalent dose rate?

    (c) What is the unit of equivalent dose rate?

    (d) Using symbols, state the relationship between **equivalent dose rate**, **equivalent dose** and the **time** of exposure, (t).

14. A person receives an absorbed dose of 40 μGy in 8 hours from a radioactive source that emits alpha particles only.
    You may wish to consult the Data Sheet.

    (a) Calculate the equivalent dose received by the person.

    (b) Calculate the equivalent dose rate received by the person.

15. A worker in the nuclear industry is subjected to emissions of 200 μGy from slow neutrons and 50 μGy from gamma radiation during the year.
    You may wish to consult the Data Sheet.

    (a) Calculate the equivalent dose experienced by the worker in the year.

    (b) Calculate the equivalent dose rate experienced by the worker in the year.

16. (a) What is meant by **background radiation**?

    (b) What is the average annual background radiation in the U.K.?

    (c) What is the value of the annual effective dose limit (in addition to background radiation) for a member of the public?

17. (a) Give **three** natural sources that contribute to the background radiation level.

    (b) Give **two** man-made (artificial) sources that contribute to the background radiation level.

18. Why do airline crews receive higher doses of radiation than workers at ground level?

Half-life

1. What happens to the activity of a radioactive source as time goes on?

2. What is meant by the **half-life** of a radioactive source?

3. Explain why the activity of a radioactive source is defined in terms of half-life.

4. Describe a method of measuring the half-life of a radioactive source.

5. A radioactive source, which has a half-life of 15 days, has a measured activity of 1600 kBq.

   Calculate its activity after 60 days.

6. The activity of a source drops from 200 kBq to 25 kBq in 6 years.

   Calculate the half-life of the source.

7. The initial activity from a radioisotope is 120 counts/minute.
   The half-life of the radioisotope is 4 hours.

   Calculate the time for the activity to reach a reading of 15 counts/minute.

8. A sample of radioactive iodine-131 in a medical physics laboratory had its activity monitored at the same time every week for 9 weeks.
   The background radiation count over the same period was monitored and found to be a constant 12 counts per minute.

Week	1	2	3	4	5	6	7	8	9
Recorded activity (counts/minute)	140	82.0	50.0	33.0	23.5	18.0	15.5	14.0	13.0
Corrected activity (counts/minute)									

   (a) Copy and complete the table, giving the corrected count rate for the sample each week.

   (b) Plot a graph of the corrected count rate for the sample during the period shown in the table.

   (c) Use your graph to estimate the half-life of iodine-131.

Applications of nuclear radiation

1. Desribe how a Geiger-Müller tube detects radiation.

2. Describe how film badges monitor exposure to radiation.

3. (a) What is a **gamma camera**?

   (b) Give a use for a gamma camera in medicine.

   (c) Explain the way that a gamma camera works.

4. Explain the way that a smoke detector operates.

5. Give **two** medical uses of radiation based on the fact that radiation can destroy cells.

6. (a) What is meant by a radioactive **tracer**?

   (b) Give a use for tracers:

      (i) in medicine;

      (ii) in agriculture;

      (iii) in industry.

7. (a) Why do radioisotopes used as tracers in the body have a short half-life?

   (b) (i) Which type of radiation is used?

      (ii) Explain your answer.

8. (a) Explain the way that radioisotopes are used to monitor the thickness of materials on an industrial production line, e.g. in paper making.

   (e) Which type of radiation is used?

   (c) Why does the radioisotope used have a relatively long half-life?

Fission and fusion reactions

1. Explain what is meant by **nuclear fission**.

2. Nuclear fission can be either **spontaneous** or **induced**.

   Explain the difference between these two processes.

3. (a) Describe how the process of fission is used in a nuclear reactor to produce energy.

   (b) What is the most common fuel that is used in a nuclear fission reactor?

4. Explain what is meant by a **chain reaction**.
   A diagram may help your explanation.

5. In a nuclear fission power station the heat energy produced has to be controlled.

   Describe the main principles of this operation.

6. (a) Why are there particular problems associated with the disposal of radioactive waste products from nuclear reactors?

   (b) Give an example of:

   (i) low level radioactive waste;

   (ii) high level radioactive waste.

   (c) Give a suitable disposal method for each type.

7. Explain what is meant by **nuclear fusion**.

8. Copy and complete the following sentences.

   (a) When a uranium nucleus splits up, the nucleus of atoms of two different _____ are formed, and _____ is given out. This process is known as nuclear _____.

   (b) When two nuclei of low mass combine, the nucleus of an atom of a different _____ is formed, and _____ is given out. This process is known as nuclear _____.

9. Nuclear fusion reactors are currently only at the experimental stage.

   (a) Give a major difficulty associated with the building of a fusion reactor.

   (b) Give an advantage that fusion reactors could have over fission reactors.

Velocity and displacement – vectors and scalars

Vector and scalar quantities

1. (a) What is meant by a **scalar quantity**?

   (b) What is meant by a **vector quantity**?

2. Copy and complete the table by entering the following quantities under the correct heading:
   distance; displacement; velocity; force; acceleration; energy; work done; temperature; heat; time; weight; mass; gravitational field strength; speed.

Scalar quantities	*Vector quantities*

3. (a) What is the difference between **distance** and **displacement**?

   (b) What is the difference between **speed** and **velocity**?

4. Which of the following statements relate to speed and which to velocity?

   (a) A car moving at 15 m s^{-1}.

   (b) A boat sailing due east at 0.5 m s^{-1}.

   (c) Light travels at 3 x 10^6 m s^{-1}.

   (d) The aircraft cruised at 900 kilometres per hour on a south-westerly course to South America.

5. A runner takes part in a 400 m race.
   The race starts and finishes at the same place.

   (a) What distance is covered by the runner?

   (b) What is the runner's displacement at the end of the race?

6. A car travels by road from town **X** to town **Y**.
   Town **X** is 17 km east of town **Y**. The road between the towns is 23 km long.

   (a) What distance does the car travel?

   (b) What is the displacement of town **Y** from town **X**?

Resultant of vector quantities

1. A boy walks 200 m east along a street, stops and then continues for a further 100 m in the same direction.

   (a) What is the total distance he has walked?

   (b) What is his final displacement from his starting point?

2. A boy walks 50 m south and then turns back and retraces his steps for 30 m.

   (a) What is the total distance he has walked?

   (b) What is his final displacement from his starting point?

3. A girl runs 500 m north, turns and runs 500 m east and finally turns and runs 500 m south.

   (a) What is the total distance she has run?

   (b) What is her final displacement from her starting point?

4. State what is meant by the **resultant** of a number of forces.

5. Calculate the resultant of the forces acting on each of the blocks shown. Give magnitude and direction in your answer.

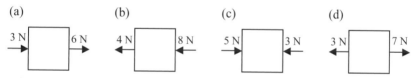

(a)   (b)   (c)   (d)

6. A plane is flying north directly into a wind of 20 m s^{-1}.
   The velocity of the plane through the air is 120 m s^{-1}.

   Calculate the resultant velocity of the plane.

7. Calculate the resultant of the forces acting on each of the blocks shown. Give magnitude and direction in your answer.

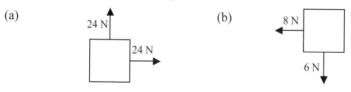

(a)   (b)

8. What can a free body diagram be used for?

9. An athlete of weight 500 N hangs from two rings as shown.
   The angle between each arm and the athlete's body is 30°.

   (a) Draw a free body diagram for the forces acting on the athlete.

   (b) By drawing a vector diagram for the forces acting on the athlete, or otherwise, find the force in each of her arms.

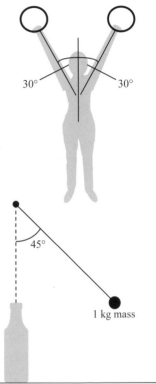

10. A game in a fairground involves a bottle being knocked down from behind by swinging a 1 kg mass on a string at it.

    (a) Draw a free body diagram for the 1 kg mass when it is pulled out by a horizontal force to 45° as shown.

    (b) By drawing a vector diagram for the forces acting, or otherwise, find the horizontal force needed to pull the mass out this far.

11. A tanker is being pulled along in the water by two tugs. Each tug exerts a force of 50 000 N on the tanker. The angle between the two chains joining the tugs to the tanker is 90°.

    Calculate the resultant force acting on the tanker.

Speed, velocity and time

1. State what is meant by:
   (a) **speed**;
   (b) **velocity**.

2. (a) State the relationship between **distance** (d), **time** (t) and **speed** (v).
   (b) What is the unit of each quantity in the expression, and its abbreviation?

3. State the relationship between **distance** (d), **time** (t) and **average speed** ($\bar{v}$).

4. (a) State the relationship between **displacement** (s), **time** (t) and **velocity** (v).
   (b) What is the unit of each quantity in the expression, and its abbreviation?

5. State the relationship between **displacement** (s), **time** (t) and **average velocity** ($\bar{v}$).

6. Describe how to measure the average speed of a runner in a race.
   Your description should include:
   the measurements that have to be made;
   the equation that is used to calculate average speed.

7. A runner completes a 110 m race on a straight race track in 12.4 s.
   Calculate the magnitude of the average velocity of the runner.

8. A cyclist travels a distance of 31 km at an average speed of 8.1 m s^{-1}.
   Calculate the time taken for the journey.

9. A motorist travels the 72 km from Edinburgh to Glasgow in a time of $1\frac{1}{4}$ hours.
   Calculate the average speed for this journey in metres per second.

10. Estimate how far a supersonic aircraft would travel in 1 minute while flying at the speed of sound.

11. (a) Explain what is meant by **instantaneous** speed.

    (b) Give an example of the measurement of instantaneous speed.

    (c) Describe how to measure the instantaneous speed of an object.
        Your description should include:
        the measurements that have to be made;
        any special points about these measurements;
        how these measurements are made;
        the equation that is used to calculate instantaneous speed.

12. (a) What is meant by **reaction time**?

    (b) Why are more accurate results of instantaneous speed obtained when
        the timing is carried out using a light gate and an electronic timer
        rather than by using a manual stopwatch?

13. Two towns are 30 km apart. Town **B** is due east of town **A**.
    The bus journey from one town to the other takes half an hour.

    (a) Calculate the average velocity, in kilometres per hour, for the bus journey
        from town **A** to town **B**.

    (b) At various times during the journey, the bus stops to pick up passengers,
        travels in heavy traffic in a town centre and travels on a motorway.
        Explain why the instantaneous speed of the bus varies between 0 and
        80 km h^{-1}.

    (c) Why are the average and instantaneous speeds of the bus different?

14. A runner completes a 15 km road race in 1 hour 40 minutes.
    The race starts and finishes at the same place.

    (a) What distance does the runner cover?

    (b) What is the runner's displacement at the end of the race?

    (c) Calculate the average speed of the runner in metres per second.

    (d) What is the average velocity of the runner?

15. A student walks from the Physics classroom to the French classroom along the
    school corridors in 3 minutes.
    The Physics classroom is 180 m directly south of the French classroom
    although the length of the corridors connecting the two classrooms is 270 m.

    (a) Calculate the average speed of the student.

    (b) Calculate the average velocity of the student.

Acceleration

1. What is meant by **acceleration**?

2. (a) What is the symbol that is used for acceleration?
   (b) What is the unit of acceleration, and its abbreviation?

3. What is the acceleration of a car that is travelling at a constant speed along a straight level road?

4. (a) What does a negative sign associated with an acceleration value signify?
   (b) What is another term used for a negative acceleration?

5. A car advertisement makes the following statement relating to the performance of the car: '0 to 26 m s^{-1} in 8.2 s'.
   What quantity do these figures for the car refer to?

6. (a) State the equation that links **acceleration, change in velocity** and the **time** for the velocity to change. Use the symbol for each quantity.
   (b) What is the unit of each quantity in the expression, and its abbreviation?

7. State the equation that links **acceleration, initial velocity, final velocity** and the **time** for the velocity to change.
   Use the symbol for each quantity in the expression.

8. Starting with the definition of acceleration, show that: $v = u + at$

9. Calculate the acceleration of a car that increases its velocity by 9.0 m s^{-1} in 5.0 s.

10. A car accelerates from rest to 28 m s^{-1} in 8.0 s.
    Calculate its acceleration.

11. Calculate the final velocity of a train that accelerates uniformly at a rate of 0.6 m s^{-2} from a velocity of 2.0 m s^{-1} for 30 s.

12. A bus travelling at 6.4 m s^{-1} brakes and comes to a stop in 4.0 s.
    Calculate its acceleration.

13. A ship has a maximum acceleration of 0.1 m s^{-2}.
    Calculate the minimum time it would take to increase its velocity from 1 m s^{-1} to 5 m s^{-1}.

14. A car, decelerating uniformly at 2 m s^{-2}, comes to rest in 10 s.
    Calculate its initial velocity.

Velocity-time graphs

1. Draw the velocity-time graph for the motion of a car that is travelling at a constant velocity of 15 m s^{-1}.

2. A car starts from rest and reaches a velocity of 10 m s^{-1} in 8 s.

   Draw the velocity-time graph for this motion.

3. The driver of a car sees the traffic lights in the distance change to red. The brakes are applied to decelerate the car uniformly. The velocity of the car reduces from 20 m s^{-1} to 5 m s^{-1} in 6 s.

   Draw the velocity-time graph for this motion.

4. State the way to calculate displacement from a velocity-time graph.

5. State the way to calculate acceleration from a velocity-time graph.

6. (a) Describe the motion represented by each of the following velocity-time graphs.

   (b) Calculate the displacement in the given time period for each graph.

   (c) Calculate the acceleration shown for each graph.

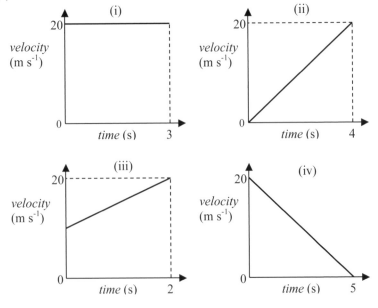

7. Consider the following velocity-time graph for the motion of a car.

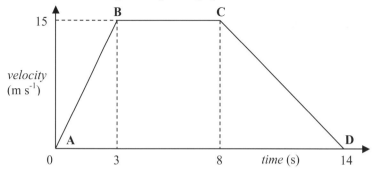

(a) Describe the motion represented by each section of this graph.

(b) What is the maximum velocity reached by the car?

(c) Calculate the acceleration shown on the graph:

    (i) in section **AB**;

    (ii) in section **CD**.

(d) Calculate the displacement of the car 14 s after the start.

8. A suburban train accelerates uniformly from rest at a station. The train reaches a velocity of 25.0 m s^{-1} in 10.0 s. It then decelerates uniformly to stop at a second station in a *further* 20.0 s.

(a) Draw the velocity-time graph for the motion of the train.

(b) Calculate the acceleration of the train.

(c) Calculate the deceleration of the train.

(d) How far apart are the two stations?

9. A trolley is given a push and moves down a sloping runway with a starting velocity of 1.0 m s^{-1}.
After 1.0 s, when the velocity has reached 2.0 m s^{-1}, it meets a horizontal part of the runway and takes a *further* 2.0 s to come to rest.

(a) Draw the velocity-time graph for the motion of the trolley.

(b) Calculate the total length of the runway used by the trolley.

Newton's laws

Force

1. (a) What is the symbol that is used for **force**?

   (b) What is the unit of force, and its abbreviation?

2. State whether force is a scalar quantity or a vector quantity.

3. Describe **three** effects that a force can have on an object.

4. (a) Describe the way that a newton balance is used to measure force.

   (b) Give a use for a newton balance.

5. What is meant by **friction**?

6. (a) Describe **three** situations where the force of friction is useful.

   (b) Explain how the force of friction can be increased in each of these situations.

7. (a) Describe **three** situations where the force of friction is unwanted.

   (b) Explain how the force of friction can be decreased in each of these situations.

Balanced forces and Newton's first law

1. What is meant by **balanced forces** acting on an object?

2. (a) Draw **two** diagrams to show different ways that **two** forces can act on an object and yet have the same effect as no force at all.

   (b) Draw a diagram to show a way that **three** forces can act on an object and yet have the same effect as no force at all.

3. A block of wood is on a bench.

   What can be said about the forces that are acting on the block?

4. A car is travelling at a constant velocity along a straight, level road.

   (a) What can be said about the forces acting on the car?

   (b) Explain why the car engine needs to be running to maintain the constant velocity.

5. Explain why you continually have to pedal a bicycle to move at a constant velocity along a straight, level road.

6. State **Newton's First Law of Motion**.

7. (a) What happens to the velocity of an object when it has no forces acting on it?

    (b) What happens to the velocity of an object when it has balanced forces acting on it?

8. Use Newton's First Law of Motion to explain the following situations.

    (a) A book sitting on a table does not move.

    (b) A car can travel along a straight level road at a constant velocity.

    (c) A spaceship in outer space continues moving at the same velocity.

9. (a) What is the purpose of seat belts in a car?

    (b) Explain why seat belts in a car prevent passengers from being injured.

Unbalanced force and Newton's Second Law

1. What is the effect of an unbalanced (or resultant) force on an object?

2. State what happens to the motion of an object:

    (a) when its mass decreases while the unbalanced force acting on it remains the same;

    (b) when the unbalanced force acting on it increases.

3. A car is travelling at a constant velocity along a straight, level road.

    What will happen to the motion of the car when an unbalanced force is applied to it?

4. A student on a skateboard is travelling at a constant velocity along a straight, level track. A friend jumps on to the skateboard.

    Explain what happens to the motion of the skateboard.

5. A hot air balloon is falling at a constant velocity in the air.
    A balloonist throws a sandbag overboard.

    Describe what happens to the balloon.

6. What is meant by the **mass** of an object?

7. (a) What is the symbol that is used for mass?

    (b) What is the unit of mass, and its abbreviation?

8. (a) State the relationship between **acceleration, mass** and **unbalanced** or
        resultant force. Use the symbol for each quantity in the expression.

    (b) What is the unit of each quantity, and its abbreviation?

9. Define the unit of force, the newton.

10. State **Newton's Second Law of Motion**.

11. A trolley of mass 0.75 kg is acted upon by an unbalanced force of 3.0 N.
    Calculate its acceleration.

12. Calculate the unbalanced force that will produce an acceleration of 5 m s^{-2} in
    a mass of 2 kg.

13. An unbalanced force of 1500 N causes a car to decelerate at 2.40 m s^{-2}.
    Calculate the mass of the car.

14. A car of mass 1200 kg is being driven along a straight, level road. The engine
    supplies a driving force of 2500 N and the total resistive forces due to friction
    and air resistance amount to 700 N.

    (a) Draw a diagram showing these forces acting on the car.

    (b) Calculate the acceleration of the car.

15. A parachutist with parachute has a total mass of 120 kg.
    The parachutist has a downward acceleration of 0.10 m s^{-2}.

    Calculate the unbalanced force acting on the parachutist.

Work done, force and distance/displacement

1. Copy and complete the following sentence.

   When an object is moved, the amount of work that is done is a measure of the ——— transferred.

2. (a) What is the symbol that is used for all types of **energy**?

   (b) What is the unit of energy and its abbreviation?

   (c) What are the **two** symbols for work done?

3. (a) State the relationship between **work done**, **unbalanced force** and **distance** moved by an object.
   Use one of the symbols for work done and the symbols for each of the other two quantities in the expression.

   (b) What is the unit of each quantity, and its abbreviation?

4. A force of 5.0 N is used to move a box a distance of 3.0 m along a bench.
   Calculate the work done by the force.

5. A force moves a box 21 m by doing 1197 J of work.
   Calculate the size of the force.

6. A force of 50 N is applied to an object and 210 J of work is done.
   Calculate the distance that the force moves the object in the direction of the force.

7. (a) State the relationship between **power**, **work done** and **time**.
   Use the symbol for each quantity in the expression.

   (b) What is the unit of each quantity, and its abbreviation?

8. A force transfers 360 J in 1 minute.
   Calculate the power involved.

9. (a) Using two relationships involving work done, obtain the relationship between force, distance/displacement, time and power.

   (b) Show that this expression can be used to obtain a relationship between force, speed/velocity and power.

10. A small electric motor lifts a mass of 0.3 kg at a constant velocity of 20 cm s^{-1}.
    Calculate the power developed by the motor.

11. What type of energy is gained by an object when work is done to lift it?

12. Copy and complete the following sentence.

    The work done against gravity is equal to the increase in ———————
    ——————— ——————— of an object.

13. Under what circumstances is work done on an object by gravity?

14. A crane lifts a crate of mass 61 kg through a height of 25 m in a time of 1 minute.

    (a) Calculate the gravitational potential energy gained by the crate.

    (b) Ignoring the mass of the crane jib, calculate the output power of the crane.

    (c) The cable of the crane breaks when it has completed the lifting operation.

    Calculate the maximum speed of the crate just as it reaches the ground (ignoring air resistance).

Gravitational field strength

1. What is meant by the **weight** of an object?

2. (a) What is the symbol that is used for weight?

   (b) What is the unit of weight, and its abbreviation?

3. (a) What is the name of the force that acts on an object because of its mass?

   (b) What can be said about the acceleration of all objects near the surface of the Earth due to this force acting on the objects, if the effects of friction can be ignored?

4. State the approximate value of the acceleration due to gravity near the surface of the Earth.

5. What is a **gravitational field**?

6. What is meant by **gravitational field strength**?

7. What is the value of the gravitational field strength near the surface of the Earth?

8. Explain the difference between **mass** and **weight**.
In your explanation, state which of these quantities is a constant and which can vary, and explain why this is so.

9. (a) State the relationship between **weight, mass** and **gravitational field strength**.
Use the symbol for each quantity in the expression.

(b) What is the unit of each quantity, and its abbreviation?

10. Show that acceleration due to gravity and gravitational field strength are both numerically equal.

11. What is the approximate answer when the weight of an object near the surface of the Earth is divided by its mass?

12. Calculate the weight on Earth of a person who has a mass of 52 kg.

13. Calculate the weight of a 1 kg bag of sugar.

14. When weighed on a public weighbridge, the weight of a lorry is found to be 98 000 N.
Calculate the mass of the lorry.

15. A person of mass 58 kg runs up a flight of stairs in 9.0 s.
The vertical height of the stairs is 5.1 m.

(a) Calculate the weight of the person.

(b) Calculate the work done.

(c) Calculate the power developed by the person in running up the stairs.

16. Copy and complete the following statements using the following words:
decreased; increased; unchanged; zero.

A block of metal has a mass of 1 kg on Earth.

(a) If the block was taken to the Moon where the gravitational field strength is 1.6 N kg^{-1} its mass would be ———— and its weight would be ————.

(b) If the block was taken to Jupiter where the gravitational field strength is 23 N kg^{-1} its mass would be ———— and its weight would be ————.

(c) If the block was taken into space, far away from any planets, its mass would be ———— and its weight would be ————.

17. It might be possible, although unlikely, for an astronaut of the future to go 'space-hopping' from planet to planet. Consider the combined mass of the astronaut and spacesuit to be 122 kg.

    What would be the total weight of the astronaut and spacesuit on each of the planets given in the table?

Planet	Gravitational field strength ($N\ kg^{-1}$)
Venus	8.9
Earth	9.8
Mars	3.7
Jupiter	23.0

18. A piece of equipment that has a weight of 25 N on Earth is taken to the Moon where the acceleration due to gravity is $1.6\ m\ s^{-2}$.

    Calculate its weight on the Moon.

19. Under what conditions is an object **weightless**?

20. An object can sometimes appear weightless when it is not actually so.

    Explain how this can be.

21. Copy and complete the following sentences using a word or a phrase from the list:
    acceleration due to gravity; gravitational field strength; inertia; mass; weight.

    (a) The amount of matter in an object is known as its ————.

    (b) The force of gravity acting on an object is known as its ————.

    (c) Any object that has a mass also has a reluctance to have its motion changed.
    This property is known as its ————.

    (d) The ratio of weight to mass for an object close to the surface of a planet is known as that planet's ————.

    (e) Although they have different units, two quantities are equivalent to each other.
    These quantities are gravitational field strength and ————.

22. What happens to the weight of a body as it gets further away from the surface of Earth?

23. What is meant by **thrust**?

24. A booster rocket motor is fired on a spacecraft which is far away in deep space.
The rocket motor supplies a thrust of 2.0×10^3 N.
The mass of the spacecraft is 5.0×10^3 kg.

Calculate the acceleration produced.

25. (a) Explain why a rocket motor does **not** need to be kept on all the time while the rocket is moving in deep space.

(b) What happens to a rocket in deep space when the rocket motor is fired?

26. (a) Explain what is meant by **terminal velocity**.

(b) Use Newton's First Law of Motion to explain why an object in free-fall reaches terminal velocity.

27. Explain why using a parachute reduces the terminal velocity of a falling object.

Newton's Third Law

1. What causes a rocket in space to move forward?

2. 'A exerts a force on B, B exerts an equal but opposite force on A.'

   Use the above rule to explain:

   (a) how a car moves forward along a road;

   (b) how a chair can support a person sitting on it;

   (c) how a rocket moves forward in space.

   In each case, draw a diagram with forces included, and state which object you mean as A and which object you mean as B.

3. State **Newton's Third Law of Motion**.

4. What is meant by **'Newton Pairs'**?

5. Identify the 'Newton Pairs' acting on the helicopter shown.

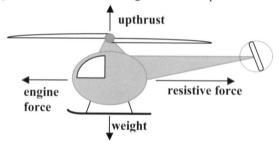

6. Identify the 'Newton Pairs' acting on the boat shown.

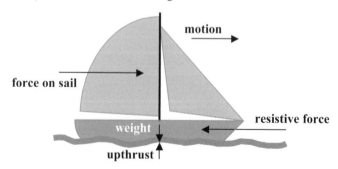

7. Although they are different, 'Newton Pairs' are often confused with balanced forces.

   Explain clearly the difference between balanced forces and 'Newton Pairs'.

Projectile motion

1. An object projected horizontally does **not** continue to move horizontally.

    (a) Describe the path that it takes.

    (b) Explain what causes it to follow this path.

2. The path of a projectile can be treated as two independent motions.

    (a) Describe and explain the horizontal motion of a projectile.

    (b) Describe and explain the vertical motion of a projectile.

3. There is only one quantity that is common to the vertical and horizontal motions of a projectile.

    What is this quantity?

4. A food parcel is dropped from a helicopter that is flying horizontally at a constant speed of 55 m s^{-1}. The parcel takes 4.0 s to reach the ground.

    Ignoring air resistance:

    (a) state the horizontal speed of the parcel just as it reaches the ground;

    (b) calculate the horizontal distance travelled by the parcel;

    (c) calculate the vertical speed of the parcel just as it reaches the ground;

    (d) calculate the height of the helicopter when the parcel was dropped.

5. By considering the motion of a projectile, explain why a satellite remains in orbit.

6. Describe and explain **Newton's thought experiment**.

Space exploration

Our understanding of the universe and planet Earth

1. (a) Give **three** ways that space exploration has advanced our understanding of **the universe**.

    (b) State the **two** main sources that provide evidence to support our current understanding.

2. (a) Why are different kinds of telescopes needed to detect the signals that come to Earth from space?

    (b) Give **three** different kinds of telescope.

3. Give **three** ways that space exploration has increased our understanding of **planet Earth**.

4. Write a short paragraph on the contribution of space exploration to environmental research in the study of:

    (a) studying air quality;

    (b) climate change;

    (c) alternative energy;

    (d) near-Earth objects.

5. Explain the way that space exploration has increased our awareness of the natural resources of planet Earth.

6. Give **three** developments that have benefitted from space exploration in the areas of:

    (a) medicine;

    (b) technology;

    (c) agriculture.

7. Write a short paragraph on the use of data collected by satellites being used to benefit:

    (a) wildlife preservation and conservation of natural habitats;

    (b) weather forecasting.

8. Space exploration can help predict and locate natural disasters.

    Give **three** examples of a natural disaster that can be predicted and located.

9. (a) What type of energy does a spacecraft have because of its movement?

    (b) (i) What energy transformation takes place when the spacecraft re-enters the Earth's atmosphere from space?

       (ii) What causes this energy transformation to take place?

10. There are risks associated with manned space exploration.

    (a) Give a risk associated with take-off.

    (b) Give **two** risks to astronauts when the craft is in space.

    (c) (i) What is the main risk associated with re-entry to the atmosphere of the Earth?

       (ii) Give a method that could be used to reduce the risk.

    (d) Give a risk associated with the landing after re-entry.

Calculations

1. The orbiter part of a Space Shuttle, the part that returns to Earth after the space mission, has a mass of 72 000 kg. While in orbit, its speed is 8500 m s^{-1} and at touchdown its speed is 94 m s^{-1}.

   (a) Calculate the kinetic energy of the orbiter while it is in orbit.

   (b) Calculate the kinetic energy of the orbiter just as it touches down.

   (c) What has happened to the 'lost' kinetic energy between being in orbit and at touchdown?

   (d) The average force needed to stop the orbiter as it travels along the runway between touchdown and coming to rest is 180 kN.

   Calculate the length of the runway needed.

2. A meteorite consists of a lump of iron of mass 3.0 kg. It enters the atmosphere of the Earth at 2000 m s^{-1}.

   Assuming 10 % of the kinetic energy of the meteorite is converted into heat (which in fact does not happen), calculate the rise in temperature of the meteorite.

Satellites

1. What is a **satellite**?

2. Name the one natural satellite of the Earth.

3. Three types of orbit used by satellites are described as **low Earth orbit**, **polar orbit** and **geostationary orbit**.

   Explain what is meant by each of these types of orbit.

4. The table shows three types of orbit used by satellites around the Earth.

Type of orbit	Function of satellite
low Earth orbit	
polar orbit	
geostationary orbit	

   For each type of orbit, name **two** functions of satellites that use the orbit, using the following list:
   communications satellite; **Earth observation satellite**; **spy satellite**; **weather satellite**.

   (You will have to include two functions twice in the table.)

5. (a) What is meant by the **period** of a satellite?

   (b) What does the period of a satellite depend upon?

6. The table gives information about the height (altitude) and the period of orbit of different low Earth orbit satellites.

Altitude (km)	Period (minutes)
160	88
	100
2000	127

   Estimate the altitude of the satellite that has a period of 100 minutes.

7. Why is world-wide communication difficult without the use of satellites?

8. Describe how telecommunication from one continent to another is possible using geostationary satellites and ground stations.

9. (a) What is the purpose of **parabolic reflectors** on aerials and receivers?

   (b) Explain how parabolic reflectors on aerials and receivers do their job. Use a labelled diagram to help your explanation.

10. Describe an application of parabolic reflectors used in telecommunication. In your description you should mention:
    satellites;
    microwave links;
    repeater stations;
    boosters.

11. Use a labelled diagram to explain why parabolic reflectors are used with some transmitters.

12. A spy satellite in an orbit of 1500 km above Earth sends a radio signal to a receiving station directly below it on the surface of the Earth.

    Calculate the time it takes the signal to reach Earth.

Changes in state

1. Name the **three** states of matter.

2. (a) What **two** changes can be experienced by an object when heat is
transferred to it?

   (b) Explain how to decide which of the two changes will happen in any
particular case.

3. (a) Copy and complete the diagram, using the following words:
condensation; freezing; fusion; vaporisation

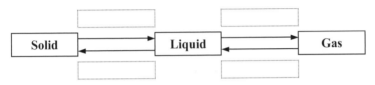

   (b) What does **not** change when the state of a substance is changing?

4. (a) What must be transferred to a substance to make it change state from a
solid to a liquid or from a liquid to a gas?

   (b) What is transferred from a substance when its state changes from a gas to
a liquid or from a liquid to a solid?

5. (a) Give **two** applications that involve a change of state.

   (b) Explain the way that each application works.

6. (a) What does the word '**latent**' mean?

   (b) Hence explain what is meant by '**latent heat**'.

7. (a) Give another word that means the same as 'fusion'.

   (b) Give another word that is often used for 'vaporisation'.

8. (a) What is meant by the **latent heat of fusion** of a substance?

   (b) What is meant by the **latent heat of vaporisation** of a substance?

9. (a) State the equation that links **heat** to the **mass** and the **specific latent heat**
of a substance.
Use the symbol for each quantity in the expression.

   (b) What is the unit of each quantity, and its abbreviation?

10. Calculate the heat needed to convert 0.500 kg of water at its boiling point into steam.

11. Calculate the heat removed when 0.500 kg of water freezes to ice at 0 °C.

12. A substance is solid at room temperature. The graph shows how the temperature of the substance changes as it is heated from 0 °C to 400 °C.

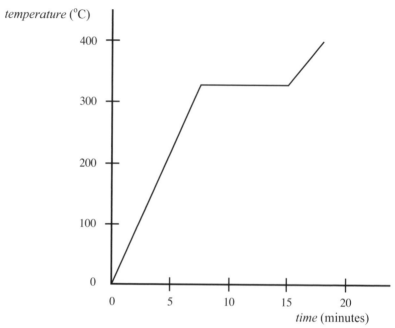

(a) What is the approximate melting point of the substance?

(b) The mass of the substance is 0.44 kg.
1.1 x 10^4 J of heat energy was supplied to the substance while it changed state.

Calculate the specific latent heat of the substance.

13. Water in the form of a lump of ice is removed from a freezer at a temperature of -18.0 °C. The mass of the ice is 1.00 kg.

Calculate the heat energy that must be transferred to the water in order to completely convert it to steam at 100 °C.

Cosmology

Light year

1. What is the value of the speed of light in air (vacuum)?

2. State the approximate time it takes light to travel to Earth from:
   (a) the Sun;
   (b) the next nearest star, Proxima Centauri;
   (c) the furthest edge of our galaxy.

3. What is the unit 'light year' used to measure?

4. Calculate the magnitude of one light year, in SI units.

5. Explain why it is necessary to use a light year as a unit in astronomy.

The observable universe

1. State what is meant by:
   (a) a planet;   (b) a moon;
   (c) a star;   (d) the solar system;
   (e) an exoplanet;   (f) a galaxy;
   (g) the universe.

2. Copy and complete the following sentences using words from the list:
   exoplanet; galaxy; Milky Way; moon; planet; solar system; star; sun; universe.

   (You will have to use some words more than once and sometimes use the plural of the word.)

   (a) The ————— consists of a large number of —————, such as the ————— and Andromeda, each separated by empty space.

   (b) Each ————— consists of millions of —————, of which Proxima Centauri is the second closest to Earth, the closest to Earth being —————.

(c) Earth is one of eight ————, each of which orbits around the
      ————. Such a group of heavenly bodies is known as a ————.

(d) With continuing space exploration, we are discovering more and more
      ———— orbiting around ————. Over one thousand have so far
      been discovered. Some may have even been discovered outside our own
      galaxy, the ————.

(e) Like the Earth, some of the ———— in our own and in other
      ———— have natural satellites which orbit around them.
      These satellites are called ————.

3. Copy and complete the following sentences.

   (a) The collection of all known galaxies is called the ————.

   (b) A ———— consists of a large number of stars and solar systems.

   (c) A heavenly body which emits light and heat energy is called a
        ————.

   (d) The nearest star to the Earth is ————.

   (e) Some stars, like the Sun, have several ———— orbiting round them.

   (f) A star, together with the heavenly bodies associated with it, is collectively
        known as a ————.

   (g) Some planets have one or more natural satellites, which are called
        ————, orbiting round them.

4. Space exploration has allowed scientists to determine the origin and age of the
    universe.

   (a) Name the theory that is now being used to describe the way that the
        universe began.

   (b) Briefly describe what this theory states.

   (c) Approximately how long ago did the described event happen?

5. (a) What is the evidence to support the current theory about the origin and
        age of the universe?

   (b) How is this evidence being obtained?

Spectra

1. (a) Explain what is meant by a **continuous spectrum**.

   (b) Draw a fully labelled diagram to show how a prism splits white light into a continuous spectrum.

2. Name an optical instrument that uses a prism (or a diffraction grating) to allow a spectrum to be observed.

3. (a) Explain what is meant by a **line spectrum**.

   (b) How is a line spectrum produced?

   (c) Explain why line spectra are useful.

4. (a) Name **two** types of line spectra.

   (b) What does each look like?

5. The line emission spectra for hydrogen and helium are shown.

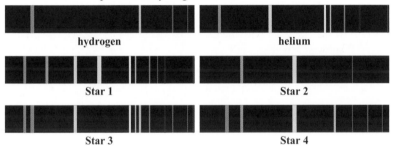

A scientist uses a spectroscope to view the light from four different stars.

   (a) Which star contains **neither** hydrogen nor helium?

   (b) Which star contains hydrogen but **not** helium?

   (c) Which star contains helium but **not** hydrogen?

   (d) Which star contains **both** hydrogen and helium?

6. (a) What is meant by **redshift**?

   (b) What does redshift indicate about the universe?

Open-ended questions

1. Two friends from primary school noticed that a lamp in a house light was not working. One told the other that " You can't take the lamp out, because the electricity will flow out of the circuit like water out of a pipe."

   Use your knowledge of Physics to explain why the lamp can be replaced without losing electricity.

2. Anne uses a mains-powered hairdryer in her bedroom. The hairdryer has a fan which blows air that has been heated by a heater. In case the flow of air is restricted, there is a thermal switch in series with the heater. Anne notices that when she lays the hairdryer down on the bedclothes, the hairdryer stops working. It starts again after a few minutes. Anne thinks that there may be a break in the cable, but Jonny says it is more likely to do with the hairdryer overheating.

   Use your knowledge of Physics to decide which explanation is more likely.

3. Your friend reads in an online report that scientists "... *found conclusive evidence that solar panels ... are draining the Sun of its energy.*" You realise that this report is a hoax.

   Use your knowledge of Physics and of photovoltaic cells to explain to your friend why this report is a hoax.

4. A refrigerator is left working with its door open in a perfectly heat-sealed room – a room where no heat can enter or leave (if such a room were to exist).

   Use your knowledge of Physics to explain whether the temperature in the room will increase, decrease or stay the same.

5. At a sporting event, spectators can buy a device that allows them to see over the heads of the crowds in front of them.

   Use your knowledge of Physics to explain the way that this device works.

6. Use your knowledge of Physics to explain why a parabolic reflector is used in a torch.
   A diagram will help your explanation.

7. A student knows that the gravitational force on a 4 kg object is greater than the gravitational force on a 2 kg object. The student reasons that when these objects are allowed to fall freely from the same height the 4 kg object has a greater acceleration. The 4 kg object should therefore have a greater speed just before it hits the ground.

   Use your knowledge of Physics to show whether the student is correct or not.

8. Different methods are used to ensure the timing of athletics races are fair for all competitors. Runners in a short distance sprint race often have loudspeakers in their starting blocks that relay the sound of the starter's pistol. The many thousands of runners in a marathon race all cross the starting line at different times so they each carry an electronic timing chip.

   Use your knowledge of Physics to explain why both methods are appropriate and fair for timing the respective races.

9. An engineering magazine invited its readers to submit a short article with the title "*The Force of Friction – Friend or Foe*".

   Use your knowledge of Physics to write a suitable article.

10. A recent newspaper report into a car accident stated that: "*The passengers, who were wearing seat belts, were not hurt but the driver, who was not wearing a seat belt, was thrown forward when the car came to a sudden halt.*"

    Use your knowledge of Physics to comment on this newspaper report.

11. In a well-known novel, some boys start a fire with some dry material by using a lens from the spectacles of their short-sighted friend to concentrate the Sun's rays.

    Use your knowledge of Physics to comment on this episode from the novel.

12. A student says that all objects in freefall from the same height have the same acceleration. The student reasons therefore that all objects will have the same kinetic energy just before reaching the ground.

    Use your knowledge of Physics to show whether the student is correct or not.

13. On a very cold day a wooden gatepost and a metal gate are both at the same temperature. You observe that when you touch them, without wearing gloves, the metal gate feels colder than the wooden gate post.

    Use your knowledge of Physics to explain this effect.

14. A student states that geostationary satellites stay above the same point on the Earth because they are in an orbit where there is no gravitational force from the Earth.

    Use your knowledge of Physics to show whether the student is correct or not.

15. One way of classifying stars is by analysing the light that the star emits.

    Use your knowledge of Physics to explain this method of classifying stars, and mention how our Sun is classified.

16. Scientists believe that the main condition required for an exoplanet (and for that matter, our own planet Earth) to sustain life is surface liquid water. They also think that there are several other conditions necessary for a planet to potentially develop and sustain life.

    Use your knowledge of Physics to list **four** other necessary conditions.

17. In describing potentially 'habitable' planets, scientists have defined a continuously habitable zone (CHZ) around a star. The continuously habitable zone around a star is sometimes called the Goldilocks Zone.

    Use your knowledge of Physics to explain what is meant by the CHZ and your knowledge of the children's fairy tale "Goldilocks and the Three Bears" to explain why it is given this name.

Answers to Numerical Questions

Unit 1   Electricity and Energy

Conservation of energy

Potential and kinetic energy *page 2*

2. 760 J
3. 180 000 J (180 kJ)
4. 2 MJ every second (to 1 significant figure)
8. 1.5 J
9. Car: 270 400 J
    Lorry: 253 500 J
    The car has the greater kinetic energy.
10. 1300 J
12. (a) 40 m s^{-1}

Electrical charge carriers and electric fields

Electrical charge and electrical current *page 4*

12. 3 A
13. 900 C
14. 4 x 10^4 s

Ohm's law

Resistance

page 8

7. (c) 56 Ω

Calculations

page 10

1. (a) (ii) 0.48 A

   (b)

Resistance of lamp (Ω)
5
5
5.3
6.8
10
14

2. 4 Ω

3. 0.05 A (50 mA)

4. 10 V

5. 180 Ω

Practical electrical and electronic circuits

Electrical and electronic components

page 13

11. 1000 Ω

16. 0.3 A

18. 400 Ω

Series and parallel circuits

page 16

5.   **1**   3 A   **2**   4 V
    3   3 A   **4**   4 V
    5   3 A   **6**   4 V

10.   **1**   3 A   **2**   1 A
    3   12 V   **4**   1 A
    5   12 V   **6**   1 A
    7   12 V

Resistors in circuits
page 19

2. (a) 100 Ω
   (b) 125 Ω

3. 12.5 Ω

5. (a) 6.7 Ω
   (b) 1.25 Ω

6. 4 Ω

7. 74 Ω

Potential divider circuits
page 20

3. 4.95 V
4. (b) 1.0 V

Electrical power

Power, energy and time
page 25

5. 9000 J (9 kJ)

6. (c) 11.3 kWh

8. (a) 100 kWh
   (b) £10.00
   (c) 1000 kWh

Power, voltage, current and resistance in electrical circuits
page 26

3. (a)

Current (A)
6.0
0.43
4.0
1.3

   (b) (i) 13 A fuse

4. 36 W

5. 3 A

6. 0.25 J every second

7. 960 Ω

9. 1.0×10^{-8} W

11. 0.75 W

12. 29 Ω

13. (a) 2.5 A
    (b) 3 A fuse

Specific heat capacity

Calculations *page 29*

7. 9020 J
8. 585 000 J (585 kJ)
10. 60 °C
11. 228 s
12. (b)   32 °C

Gas laws and the kinetic model

Pressure *page 31*

5. 74 000 Pa (74 kPa) (to 2 significant figures)
6. 5×10^6 Pa (5000 kPa)

The gas laws: volume and pressure *page 34*

6. 10 litres
7. 0.99×10^5 Pa

Different temperature scales *page 35*

4. (a) (i) 0 K   (ii) 300 K   (iii) 373 K
   (b) (i) –273 °C   (ii) 0 °C   (iii) 127 °C

The gas laws: pressure and temperature *page 36*

6. 2.2×10^5 Pa
7. 2×10^5 Pa

The gas laws: volume and temperature *page 37*

6. 0.15 m^3
7. 27 °C

The gas laws: the combined gas equation *page 38*

3. 0.91 m^3

Unit 2

Waves and Radiation

Wave parameters and behaviours

Calculations

page 41

1. 340 Hz
3. 4.8 s
5. 1700 m (1.7 km)
6. 340 m s^{-1}
7. 1020 m
8. 4 s
9. 1500 m s^{-1}
10. 5200 m s^{-1}
11. 2.2 m s^{-1}
12. 15 m
13. 3.5 s
15. 4 m s^{-1}
16. 1.3 m
17. 0.5 Hz
18. 1.1 x 10^{10} Hz

Electromagnetic spectrum

Applications of the electromagnetic spectrum

page 45

2. 4.55 x 10^{14} Hz
12. 3.6 x 10^{8} m
13. 330 m
14. 1546 kHz

Nuclear radiation

Dosimetry

page 50

4. 75 600

5. 4 MBq

8. 1 J

14. (a)   800 μSv
    (b)   100 μSv h^{-1}

15. (a)   650 μSv
    (b)   650 μSv per year

Half-life

page 53

5. 100 kBq

6. 2 years

7. 12 hours

8. (c)   about 1.15 weeks (= 8 days)

Velocity and displacement – vectors and scalars

Vector and scalar quantities   *page 56*

5. (a) 400 m
   (b) 0

6. (a) 23 km
   (b) 17 km west

Resultant of vector quantities   *page 57*

1. (a) 300 m
   (b) 300 m east

2. (a) 80 m
   (b) 20 m south

3. (a) 1500 m
   (b) 500 m east

5. (a) 9 N to the right
   (b) 12 N to the left
   (c) 2 N to the right
   (d) 4 N to the right

6. 100 m s^{-1} north

7. (a) 34 N at 45°
   (b) 10 N at 37°

9. (b) 289 N

10. (b) 10 N

11. 70 711 N

Speed, velocity and time

7. 8.87 m s^{-1}

8. 3800 seconds (just under 64 minutes)

9. 16 ms^{-1}

10. 20 400 m (20.4 km)

13. (a) 60 km h^{-1}

14. (a) 15 000 m
    (b) 0
    (c) 2.5 m s^{-1}
    (d) 0

15. (a) 1.5 m s^{-1}
    (b) 1.0 ms^{-1} north

Acceleration

9. 1.8 m s^{-2}

10. 3.5 m s^{-2}

11. 20 m s^{-1}

12. -1.6 m s^{-2}

13. 40 s

14. 20 m s^{-1}

Velocity-time graphs

6. (i)   (b) displacement = 60 m   (c) acceleration = 0 m s^{-2}
    (ii) (b) displacement = 40 m   (c) acceleration = 5 m s^{-2}
    (iii) (b) displacement = 30 m   (c) acceleration = 5 m s^{-2}
    (iv) (b) displacement = 50 m   (c) acceleration = -4 m s^{-2}

7. (b) 15 m s^{-1}
    (c) (i) 5 m s^{-2}
        (ii) -2.5 m s^{-2}
    (d) 142.5 m

8. (b) 2.5 m s^{-2}
    (c) -1.25 m s^{-2}
    (d) 375 m

9. (b) 3.5 m

Answers to Numerical Questions

Newton's laws

Unbalanced force and Newton's Second Law   *page 65*

11. 4 m s^{-2}

12. 10 N

13. 625 kg

14. (b) 1.5 m s^{-2}

15. 12 N downwards

Work done, force and distance/displacement   *page 67*

4. 15 J

5. 57 N

6. 4.2 m

8. 6 W

10. 0.6 W

14. (a) 15 000 J (15 kJ)
     (b) 250 W
     (c) 22 m s^{-1}

Gravitational field strength   *page 68*

12. 510 N

13. 10 N

14. 10 000 kg

15. (a) 570 N
     (b) 2900 J
     (c) 320 W

17. Venus   1100 N
     Earth   1200 N
     Mars   450 N
     Jupiter   2800 N

18. 4.1 N

24. 0.4 m s^{-2}

Projectile motion

page 73

4. (a) 55 m s^{-1}
   (b) 220 m
   (c) 39 m s^{-1}
   (d) 78 m

Space exploration

Calculations

page 76

1. (a) 2.6 x 10^{12} J
   (b) 3.2 x 10^8 J
   (d) 1800 m (1.8 km)

2. 420 °C

Satellites

page 77

12. 5 ms

Changes in state

page 79

10. 1.13 x 10^6 J

11. 1.67 x 10^5 J

12. (b) 2.5 x 10^4 J kg^{-1}

13. 3.05 x 10^6 J

Cosmology

Light year

page 81

4. 9.46 x 10^{15} m